# *The* Citizen *of the* World

# *The* Citizen *of the* World

OLIVER GOLDSMITH

NONSUCH

First published 1762
Copyright © in this edition 2006
Nonsuch Publishing Limited

Nonsuch Publishing Limited
73 Lower Leeson Street
Dublin 2
Ireland
www.nonsuchireland.com

National Library Cataloguing in Publication Data.
A catalogue record for this book is available from the National Library.

ISBN 1 84588 539 2

Typesetting and origination by Tempus Publishing Limited
Printed and bound in Great Britain

# Contents

# I

# Goldsmith and the Republic of Letters in 1760

In the year 1760, when the 'Chinese Letters', afterwards collected as the *Citizen of the World*, began to appear in *The Public Ledger*, Oliver Goldsmith, arrived at the thirty-second year of his age, was living in a garret in Green Arbour Court, London, and writing for the newspapers. His life had been hitherto the romance of the commonplace. Born of a family of poor clergymen-farmers, he came out of the wilderness, from the village of Pallas, County Longford, Ireland, 'a spot', remarks Macaulay, 'almost as remote from the busy and splendid capital, in which his later years were passed, as any clearing in Upper Canada, or any sheep-walk in Australasia now is'—or was in Macaulay's day. Small-pox at the village school scarred him for life; and then, branded with ugliness, he passed with a sizarship to Trinity College, Dublin, dragging-out his existence in alternations of dissipation and distress, in one long-continued battle with authority. In 1749 he came out from college, graduated in due course, but always an untaught man. There followed three years of vagabond idleness, when visions of the clerical and legal professions floated before his imagination, and dissolved, as visions will. With hopes of a medical degree he passed to Edinburgh, and thence to Leyden, and failed everywhere; but never was a man, the fineness and unaffected purity of whose nature was so little impaired by changing fortune, whose personality owed less to the mere accidents of existence. From Leyden he started on his European wanderings, and then came home, to herd with beggars in Axe Lane. First an apothecary's journeyman, then a struggling doctor, he was saved from starvation by the goodness of Samuel Richardson, who made him reader and corrector to the press. He then became usher in Peckham Academy, whither, as a visitor, came bookseller Griffiths, an observant man, and Goldsmith was engaged to furnish a 'few specimens of criticism'; and thus was born into the world of letters, to starve for five months on the bounty of the bookseller in Griffiths' garret, and after that in Green Arbour Court, at the top of Breakneck Steps: 'Oh, gods! gods! here in a garret, writing for bread, and expecting to be dunned for a milk-score'.

The atmosphere of squalid distress in which Goldsmith accomplished his earlier work was, in a measure, created by causes which, in that age, frequently condemned the professional author to a literary servitude, where the rewards of the pen were limited to the bare necessities of life and a book-seller's garret. For the world of letters, when Goldsmith entered it, was passing through a change of rulers. The day even of the old subscription edition was past. 'An author may now refuse an invitation to dinner, without fearing to incur a patron's displeasure, or to starve by remaining at home. He may now venture to appear in company, with just such clothes as other men generally wear, and talk even to princes with all the conscious superiority of wisdom. 'Though he cannot boast of fortune here, yet he can bravely assert the dignity of independence? Such words as these are the index of change, for Goldsmith lived what he wrote. The death of literary patronage has by some been traced to the bucolic difference of Walpole; it is, in reality, intimately associated with the wider recognition of the importance and power of the individual in the state. The century when were ripened the fruits of the English Revolution, the century which gave liberty of speech to the Periodical Press, dealt also the deathblow at the power of Maecenas in literature.

But a change so universal could not well be immediate; and in the interregnum between the rule of patron and public, the position of the professional author was critical indeed, patronised, as he was now, 'only by his bookseller'. For the generation which was to provide sufficient audience for novelist and poet, and thus secure for them moral independence of both patron and public, was yet unborn.

Moreover, the insignificance of this reading public, a public of no numbers, limited indeed to 'the town', with its fashionable sentimental prejudices, allowed the tyranny of the patron to assume another colour. In the *Citizen of the World*, we find Goldsmith exclaiming against a novel form of literary patronage, where an author's existence is secured, though no longer by the direct bounty, by the indirect approbation of some great man, by whose word the public is entirely swayed in its opinion. Goldsmith, with good reason, champs the bit which restrains the writer in an age of false taste. He, author by hard destiny, can boast a training 'in that best of schools, the school of adversity', where he 'has grown pale in the study of nature and himself'; yet his pretensions to fame are disregarded, because they are not supported by the approbation of a lord.

Titles, moreover, have entered the lists, and an author who confesses he writes for bread, might as well send his manuscript 'to fire the baker's oven'. Goldsmith's own *History of England* secured a factitious success, by being described as 'A Series of Letters, from a Nobleman to his Son': Lords Chesterfield, Orrery, and Lyttleton were successively credited with this loose historical invention. The laborious vanities of holiday writers may offend the palate of the critical; but Time alone, the great Touchstone, can distinguish real worth, and meanwhile the professional author starves.

Literature plays so prominent a figure in the 'Chinese Letters', and Goldsmith's prospect of the literary commonwealth is so coloured by the separate circumstances of his own life, that a due consideration of those circumstances is no more than necessary, in estimating the value of his iterated literary reproaches. Grounded deep, and very full of proof, are the complaints above mentioned: they were charges incident to the literary calling, which, though not peculiar to any one age, more heavily oppressed the eighteenth than they do the present century. For, out of question, the writer's lot was then cast in harder places than now: in a comparatively unlettered age, with the decay of literary patronage, and the prostitution, under the perpetual dictatorship of Walpole of the pen of the professional author entirely to the service of party, this client of the bookseller and newspaper party-man must have found the breadrace not always to the most capable or the most honest of the literary competitors.

But when Goldsmith, in his relations with 'book-answerers' and critics, to malignity opposes hard words instead of contempt; when he finds pruriency and pertness the only ready way to public favour; when he beholds the poet indigent in proportion to his genius, and the commonwealth of letters in hopeless anarchy; then it is that we seem to breathe the separate atmosphere, of Green Arbour Court, and are compelled to the remembrance that, though past thirty, our author had as yet forced himself neither into fashion, fortune, nor fame, that the great public had not yet learned where to 'lay the emphasis of praise'.

While we allow, then, that the year 1760 was for the professional author a critical time, we must bear well in mind that Green Arbour Court lent some of its squalid atmosphere to Goldsmith's tenebrous picture of literary distress; and we must recollect that against the kindly office of critic and 'book-answerer' the same reproaches have been preferred in every century, including even our own; and lastly, we must forbear to lay entirely to Goldsmith's age what was more largely due to his disposition; for man is of so cosmopolitan a nature, that age or country alone will not alter his disposition or fix his destiny. 'Mr Goldsmith,' said Mrs. Milner at Peckham, 'you had better let me keep your money for you, as I do for some of the young gentlemen.' 'In truth, madam,' answered Oliver, 'I fear there is equal need.'

From the worser evils that the 'anarchy of letters' produced we feel that Goldsmith himself was free. Smollett berated the author of the *Citizen of the World*, that some of his early articles were submitted for revision and correction to an ignorant bookseller and his termagant wife. Correction of Goldsmith's work we may well conceive necessary at such hands; for the client of the bookseller now echoes the million, and that freedom of the press, vindicated by the author of Robinson Crusoe, had come to mean freedom to be a slave, either of party or of the public. Once, when the *Bee* was unsuccessful, Goldsmith had declared his intention to throw off all connection with taste, and 'seek for reputation on the broad road'. Happily he was never forced to more than the threat of such a fatal purpose. The people he studied indeed, in the new spirit of the age, without writing down to popular ignorance and false taste. And, if his earnestness is of a certain frivolous cast, we may at least credit him with independence, and a hearty contempt of public predilections and public morality. Coarseness was the besetting sin of his age, vice that was not relieved, as in the Carolean time, by any refinement. Political morality had found its great exemplar in Robert Walpole; popular morals were so infected with the epidemic grossness, that even the least among the varied social vices were not refined into tolerance; and that same corruption which had inoculated politics, having set in among the professors of religion, had made the Church itself a scorn to all who had the sanity of view possessed by Altangi the Chinaman. Altangi's author was no reformer in the direct sense; as a philosopher he was of no school; his philosophy was entirely unschematised; Carlyle would have found him silent, because he had no 'message' to deliver; Horace Walpole did indeed discover

that his work 'tended to no moral, no edification of any kind';
nevertheless I doubt not but, when the 'fit of parts' was on him,
in that coarse age his sincere voice was heard for good.

## II

# *The Public Ledger* and 'The Chinese Letters'

It was in April, 1757, that Oliver Goldsmith, author by compulsion before he became author by profession, began to write for the newspapers; but, three years later, he had not yet got into the trade wind, when, on Saturday, January 12, 1760 appeared the first issue of a new mercantile daily paper, *The Public Ledger, or Daily Register of Commerce and Intelligence*, which consisted of four large quarto pages of four columns each, and sold for two pence-halfpenny a number. It was published at the 'Register Office, next the Great Toy Shop in St Paul's Churchyard', edited either by the dramatist Kelly, or Griffith Jones, and identified with the name of the elder Newbery. The plan of the paper was founded in a scheme to put upon record the chief items of information, to be found in about fifty of the principal metropolitan and provincial newspapers of the day. *The Public Ledger* was thus designed to serve as an index to other papers and publications, 'supplying the deficiencies of each from all the rest, yet not rendering any of them useless'. A specimen of this Index, occupying five and a half columns of the first number, furnished an alphabetical introduction to the contents of forty-three newspapers, which might all be further consulted, on the payment of a fee, at the Public Ledger Office. Though this was explained to be the grand part of the plan, 'calculated for the real use of perhaps nine parts in ten of the nation', yet in practice it was found that even a newspaper must have an individuality of its own. The wants indeed of the man of leisure were not entirely neglected at the outset; experience proved in the end, that the holiday reader was more necessary to the support of a periodical paper than the man of affairs. The accounts, therefore, of public occurrences, political essays, and, above all, 'criticism and literature', not professedly excluded even from the first number, usurped more than their intended place, and give to *The Public Ledger* a more than temporary importance.

Daniel Defoe, in his *Review*, seems to have initiated the fashion of attracting the public to the more serious news of the day, by devoting a portion of his paper to the proceedings of an imaginary Scandalous Club, being essays on fashionable follies, and topics of the hour, built round a fictitious personal framework. No newspaper would now be complete without its series of periodical essays, embracing philosophical subjects, or free comment upon occurrences in the social life of the town, with some fiction, like that of Addison's 'Spectator Club', interpenetrating the whole. The promise, therefore, that 'the man of leisure and retirement should find his account in inspecting *The Public Ledger*' was early fulfilled by the issue, 'in No. VII, of the first article of 'Sir Simeon Swift's Ranger'. In April came the 'Visitor' of 'Philanthropy Candid, Esq.'. But by that time a work of less temporary character had earned popularity with the readers of the *Ledger* under the generally received title of 'The Chinese Letters'.

The services of Goldsmith, who had written for John Newbery early in his literary career, were, from the first, retained for *The Public Ledger*, for which he was engaged to supply two articles a week at a guinea apiece, a contract apparently fulfilled during the year 1760. To Nos. VII and IX he had already contributed unsigned letters, the one on the subject of 'Intolerance', the other on 'The Goddess of Silence', when, in No. XI, on Thursday, January 24, 1760, there appeared a third letter, from a fictitious merchant in Amsterdam, introducing to the good offices of a fellow merchant in London a mandarin and traveller, a native of Leotung, in China. This was merely introductory to another letter in the same number, addressed by Lien Chi Altangi to the merchant in Amsterdam, recording the first London impressions of the Chinese Wanderer. Thus unostentatiously, there crept into *The Public Ledger*, with only an implication of further letters to follow, the first of that series of one hundred and twenty-three philosophic epistles, which are now known to us as the *Citizen of the World*.

Goldsmith's letters had already taken the chief place in the *Ledger*, when, with their fourth appearance on Friday, February 1, 1760, they were for the first time numbered, this one being called 'Letter IV'. A design which was, without doubt, at the outset merely tentative, had quickly developed into a regular series of epistles, to which Goldsmith himself did not, during their publication in the *Ledger*, give a title, but which were at that period by common consent referred to in contemporary literature as the 'Chinese Letters'.

On June 30, 1760, appeared 'Letter LI'. In reality, during these first six months of issue, there were published in *The Public Ledger* fifty-three 'Chinese Letters'; for the first two letters appeared, as we have seen, together, and another letter, No. XLVII, which was at first continued from one copy of the *Ledger* to the next, had afterwards its two parts numbered separately. From January to June, 1760, the 'Chinese Letters' were issued with regularity once, twice, or three times a week, and shared the first place in the paper with the 'Visitor' of 'Philanthropy Candid, Esq.'.

On December 29, 1760, came 'Letter XCVII'. The letter now numbered XCIII did not appear till the following January; but that now numbered CXVIII had already been issued in August. Hence, during the last six months of 1760 there were published forty-six 'Chinese Letters', their appearance being marked with irregularity in the month of November, when there were only six, and in December, when there were but three.

During 1760 there had thus appeared in all ninety-nine out of the hundred and twenty-three letters which form the *Citizen of the World*. In 1761 the number was nearly completed, by the addition of another twenty letters: six appeared in January; three in each of the four following months; the month of June was passed over; and the series was concluded by two stragglers in the months of July and August respectively. The last letter in the *Ledger*, on Friday, August 14, 1761, was numbered CXVI, so that Letters XCVIII to CXVI appeared during 1761, not nineteen letters, as at first appears, but twenty, the number CVI being used by mistake twice. Ninety-nine letters in 1760 and twenty in 1761 make the whole number introduced into the *Ledger* one hundred and nineteen.

Goldsmith, on August 14, 1761, on the occasion of the issue of his last letter, announced the forthcoming publication of the whole series, collected into 'two volumes of the usual Spectator size'. 'Some new letters', he says, 'are added, and others, which were remarkable only for being dull, are wholly omitted'—a statement which would seem to have misled some former editors of Goldsmith's works. In revising his letters for future separate publication, Goldsmith found none so remarkable for dullness as to deserve omission; and there were only four letters included in the *Citizen of the World* which had not been previously issued among the 'Chinese Letters' in *The Public Ledger*. All four were introduced towards the close of the work. One, 'A City Night Piece' (No. CXVII), was reprinted from the fourth number of Goldsmith's own periodical, *The Bee*, having there first appeared on October 27, 1759. The 'History of the Wooden-legged Soldier' (No. CXIX) had originally brightened the pages of the *British Magazine*, in June, 1760. The first appearance of the remaining two (Nos. CXXI and CXXII), if indeed they were not wholly written with a special view to this collection, I have as yet been unable to ascertain. Letter CXXI is a political essay, which might be interpolated without much alteration into any work like the 'Chinese Letters'; but the opening paragraphs at least, if not the whole, of the 'Journey to Kentish Town' (Letter CXXII) must have been specially composed for the *Citizen of the World*.

# III

# The Citizen of the World

Pursuant to the public promise made by Goldsmith in August, 1761, the 'Chinese Letters' appeared in 1762 anonymously, in two duodecimo volumes, under the title of *The Citizen of the World* or, *Letters from a Chinese Philosopher, residing in London, to his Friends in the East*.

The 'Chinese Letters' received now a title, which was appropriate and full of meaning. *The Citizen of the World* is, of course, the Wanderer Altangi, who so often in his acts shows himself cosmopolite, and a 'lover of man'. In March, 1760, writing in *The Public Ledger* on the doctrines of Confucius, Goldsmith had represented them as drawing close the bonds of society, and as teaching men 'to become citizens of the world'; the moral code of Confucius inculcated the highest ideals of the duty of man to man. Here, then, was Goldsmith forcing upon men doctrines of universal brotherhood, and anticipating what another century was to learn by hard experience of War and Revolution. He was teaching men to be citizens of the world. It is as if he had created his Chinese Philosopher to emphasise the one great virtue of universal charity and care for the individual, and had brought him to English shores to discover, where he can, this virtue in the English race. The French nation had refused assistance to its own sons, prisoners of war, rotting in English prisons. Enemies they were to England, but enemies in distress. A subscription list was opened, and all the names for relief were English. One had written these words upon the paper enclosing his benefaction: 'the mite of an Englishman, a Citizen of the World, to Frenchmen, prisoners of war, and naked'. 'Such a one, my friend,' remarks the Chinese philosopher, 'is an honour to human nature; he makes no private distinctions of party; all that are stamped with the divine image of their creator are friends to him; he is a native of the world.'

This, then, is a Citizen of the World, a man of such humanity and sensibility of nature, that his ideals are raised one degree above patriotism; who thus becomes cosmopolitan, his charity universal, and a 'lover of man'. The phrase was too happy a one to be limited in its use to the 'Chinese Letters'. In the *Gentleman's Magazine* for January, 1761, there appeared 'An Address of a Citizen of the World to the Belligerent Sovereigns, in the name of all the Subjects of Europe,' which petitioned for intervention to stay the miseries of war, and to restore to the nations the blessings of peace.

The First Edition of 1762 was 'Printed for the Author, and sold by J. Newbery', but copies of this same edition have a different title-page to each of the volumes: 'Printed for J. Newbery at the Bible and Sun in St Paul's Churchyard'. The issues are identical, save for one other external difference. In the copies 'printed for J. Newbery' the 'Editor's Preface' is inserted in its proper place in front of Vol. I.; in the copies 'printed for the author', the 'Editor's Preface' appears in Vol. II. These, therefore, may have been the first copies printed.

The essays have now been, to a considerable extent, reordered, which has the general effect of bringing together papers upon similar topics; titles are, for the first time, given to the Letters, in an appended 'Table of Contents'; a Preface has been added; and the number of the Essays has now been increased from the original one hundred and nineteen to one hundred and twenty-three. After 1762, there were no further additions. That the last essay of the collection is, in this early edition, numbered CXIX arises from errors of numeration, which were perpetuated in what is called 'The Third Edition' of 1774 (the last that Goldsmith himself saw through the press), the numbers XXV, XLIX, LVII, and CXVI being employed twice. That these are errors, and not designedly done, is evident from the fact that the essays with which the same numbers are associated, have in none of the four cases any connection each with the other. Between 1762 and 1774, there had issued from a Dublin Press (Dublin: 2 vols. 12: printed for T. Williams: 1769) an edition of the *Citizen of the World* with different errors of numeration, where the last letter appears as No. CXX.

Thus, in the editions printed in the author's lifetime, the number of essays, being once fixed, remained constant; and, after his death, of course suffered no change. The same is nearly true of the text. Between August, 1761, and their appearance as the *Citizen of the World* in 1762, the text of the 'Chinese Letters' was subjected by their author to such a thorough and painful revision, that he might well be content to let it remain to posterity the most perfect expression of the best that was in him. Considering that the first text had already appeared in print, comparison of the two would be to some a revelation in authorship. A more instructive study it would indeed be difficult to conceive than to mark with what heavy labour the perfection of ease and fluidity of diction in Goldsmith's work is attained. There is, at least, one great lesson thence to be acquired: the lesson of literary sacrifice and retrenchment. It is remarkable to observe how often the pruning of a single word will impart threefold vigour to a thought.

# IV

# Personal Framework
# of the Letters

Interwoven with the correspondence which passed between the Wanderer, Altangi, Fum Hoam of Pekin, and Altangi's son, Hingpo, we may distinguish two separate threads of action:

i. The Story of Altangi, and his English Friends.
ii. The Story of the Love of Hingpo and Zelis.

Lien Chi Altangi, a native of Honan, a Chinese mandarin and a Philosopher, arrives in England towards the close of the year 1759. A journey of seven hundred days, during which he has visited the desert places of the world, has brought him to London. He has beheld the works of Nature, left untouched by man in primeval rudeness, and now is arrived at the centre of the busy civilization of the Western World, where best is revealed Nature developed under the work of man's hand. During his whole stay, he continues a correspondence with his fellow-philosopher in the East, receiving, in return, what Fum Hoam can tell him of events at home. The moment of his arrival is clouded with news of disaster, for the first letter from Fum Hoam records how the Emperor's displeasure at his leaving China has resulted in the slavery of his wife and daughter, and the rest of his family with the exception of his son Hingpo, who has been hidden from the officers by Fum Hoam himself, and who is already started in quest of his father.

Altangi's first friend on English shores is the Man in Black, of chief importance, after Altangi himself, to the Personal Framework round which the Letters are built. He is encountered for the first time in Westminster Abbey, where, with some show of impatience, he attends to the philosophic observations of the Wanderer; it is only when, during that famous journey with Altangi, his eccentric goodness and the story of his life are revealed, that the mysterious stranger becomes a real personage in the framework of the book. In the character of the Man in Black, it is usual to find the completest revelation of the man Goldsmith, as he was known to himself. With almost painful irony Goldsmith pictured him 'reluctantly good', reviling in the very act of relieving the objects of his benevolence, attempting with no success to tighten his purse-strings against the approaches of distress, scattering his charity not only without ostentation, but with every appearance of ill-will, hiding under a mask of parsimony and prudence the real goodness of his heart, lest he should be betrayed, before faces, into open confession of well-doing.

It is in company with the Man in Black that Altangi assists at many characteristic scenes of London life: at the Play, at meetings of a Literary Club, in the Park, at Vauxhall Gardens, at a Visitation Dinner, and at Service in St. Paul's.

One evening, as they saunter together in a public walk near the city, 'gazing on the company', the Man in Black, catching Altangi by the elbow, and turning sharply out of the walk, betrays a desire to avoid some disagreeable acquaintance ; each moment their pursuer gains upon them, hunts them through every doubling, and baffles their every effort at escape. On he comes, a strange, tattered ape of fashion: his hat is pinched up with peculiar smartness; the buckle on his breast is studded with glass; his old coat is trimmed with tarnished twist; his stockings of silk are yellow with long service. It is Beau Tibbs.

together. His days on English soil are drawing to an end. It is on one of these last evenings that he meets, for the first time, the niece of his friend the Man in Black. Hingpo now arrives in London, to find Zelis, the beautiful Christian captive, escaped there before him; for the long arm of coincidence is stretched out to the full in order to catch up the threads of this slender fiction. In the niece of the Man in Black, Hingpo discovers his betrothed. At the marriage-feast there are present, besides Altangi himself, the little Beau and Mrs Tibbs, the Man in Black, and the pawnbroker's widow. There would have been further nuptials to follow, had not the unnecessary old-age courtship of the Man in Black suffered a sudden and final interruption, by a dispute as to the carving of the turkey. Hingpo and his wife are fixed in London; Altangi goes forth again upon his wanderings in the world, his city, and the Man in Black continues his companion.

# Goldsmith in
## *The Citizen of the World*

When, in 1721, Montesquieu published his *Lettres Persanes*, his manner of writing, if not altogether new, was at least not wanting the charm of novelty. Montesquieu indeed was not the author of this kind of traveller-fable: to the seventeenth-century diary of the Turkish Sultan's agent, called *Lespion dans les cours des princes chretiens*, of Marana, he owed 'much; and less, but still something, he owed to the Siamese 'spy' in Dufresny's *Amusements serieux et comiques*. But Marana and Dufresny, passing into the crucible of genius, underwent a glorious transmutation.

It is not merely that in the *Citizen of the World* we come abreast again of the Montesquieu fable: the root-idea is there, and identical; but the root-idea might have been so worked up as to have become a new thing. Such a transmutation Goldsmith did not effect. Beau Tibbs and the Man in Black, indeed, belong to him alone; and the individualities of the 'Chinese' and 'Persian Letters' are very distinct; but the composition of his picture of manners is pure Montesquieu. A merely formal imitation would have been possible, had Goldsmith never turned a page of the *Lettres Persanes*; for the exotic traveller-fable had become almost indigenous to the English soil, which had, indeed, yielded by

this a very plentiful harvest of Montesquieu imitations. But, as a
fact, the plan and technique of the *Citizen of the World* point to a
more direct literary influence than this. The political and social
gospel of Altangi, his remarks upon the habits of the people,
and upon the government, betray a direct acquaintance with
the great original, either in its French garb, or in the English
rendering of Ambrose Philips. In the 'Chinese Letters', again,
we have distinguished two interwoven threads of fiction ; in
the 'Persian Letters', the narrative of Usbek and Rica at Paris
is relieved by another story, of the anarchy among the ladies,
Zachi, Zelis, Roxana, and the rest, in Usbek's seraglio at Ispahan:
the name, Zelis, was borrowed into the 'Chinese Letters'; she is
there the heroine of a love story, which had its beginnings in
a Persian seraglio. The facsimilitude is too glaring to be coin-
cident merely: it was the theatre, the women—their beauty,
their powder and patches, their matrimonial relations, their love
of gaming—the coffeehouse, the curiosity of the inhabitants,
their religion, their funeral rites, their courts of justice, which
arrested the judgment of Usbek and Rica during their twelve
years' residence in Paris; and it is the same things, which, during
his stay of twenty-one months in London, attract the critical
observation of the Chinese Altangi. It were tedious, and here
inopportune, to detail all of even the more prominent features
of identity; to some, however, it is no more than necessary to
attach a great importance. When Goldsmith, in the *Citizen of
the World*, spoke his views upon such subjects, as the tenure of
colonies, the marriage problem, the coffeehouse, and the curiosity of the inhabitants, he was remarking features of interest
which were not inevitably matters of observation to a foreigner,
but which had already been observed, in his Parisian satire,
by Montesquieu.

The *Citizen of the World*, then, in despite of a very marked
individuality in conception and literary style at least, if not
in setting and design, must be reckoned with Madame de
Grafigny's *Lettres d'une Peruvienne*, the *Lettres Chinoises D'Argens*,

and Voltaire's *Asiatic*, as one, if at the same time the best, of that deluge of Montesquieu imitations, which, 'like a torrent whose source was inexhaustible', during the second quarter of the eighteenth century, succeeded each other without end. But it must never be forgotten, that Tibbs the immortal and the Man in Black are to be found nowhere but in Goldsmith's work.

The traveller-fable was not entirely an exotic from France; it had already formed part of the design of John Lyly's sequel to his 'Euphues' (Euphues and his England, 1580), which M. Jusserand has called 'des Lettres Persanes a rebours': for Lyly employed his fable to eulogise his country and his age; Montesquieu his, with toothless satire, to correct the time's abuses. But the setting of the Euphuistic fiction was not epistolary; the fable was not woven into any correspondence; nor was it that part of the author's design which was most eagerly fastened on by Greene, Lodge, Dickenson, and others of the imitators of Lyly. We may, I think, justly conclude, that in the *Citizen of the World* we are breathing the separate atmosphere of the *Lettres Persanes*.

While allowing, however, the general influence of the example of Montesquieu, it is still necessary to differentiate those temporary and local influences which prompted Goldsmith, writing from hand to mouth as Newbery's journeyman, to this series of 'Chinese Letters'.

The epistolary style he adopted, at a time when the 'letter' was conceived highly of, as worthy the dignity of literary treatment. To be satisfied of the universal popularity of letter-writing, it will only be necessary to consult the pages of the very journal which gave the 'Chinese Letters' to the world: here staple news and holiday wit alike were cast into the epistolary form. A life-time's correspondence, intended, as old James Howell's 'winged messengers; had been, not for the exclusive satisfaction of one answering friend, but graced and laboured to arrest the public eye, remains the most cherished relic of the fastidious hermit of Strawberry Hill. And it was not chance merely which led Richardson to lay hands on this literary form for Pamela.

The further suggestion, in January, 1760, of a letter from the Chinaman—for not at first, but only later, when these epistles began to be regularly numbered, can Goldsmith be said to have conceived the idea of a series of letters may have been immediately prompted by recollection of the éclat with which a little political squib of Horace Walpole's had, three years earlier, been acclaimed. It purported to be one of a number of letters 'from Xo Ho, a Chinese philosopher at London, to his friend Lien Chi, at Peking'; it was written on May 12, 1757, and, being sent to press next day, went through five editions in a fortnight. It is of the right Walpole quality; reflecting the high-priest of social and literary culture, as he stoops in a condescending mood to the easy correction of that brutish thing called plebs: the English are a people who have 'names' without 'ideas'; they want fixity of resolution, and are full of false and silly prepossessions; so much he shows by current events in the political world; and then he finds a sweet fresh spring of ridicule in the anomalous relations which subsist between a king and his ministry; and another he discovers in the king's yearly 'going into the country' to Kensington; and ambles on so, superior to time and place.

More than two years after this, and a few months only before the inception of the 'Chinese Letters', Goldsmith, writing on August 14, 1759, to an Irish crony, Bob Bryanton, companion of many a wild drinking-bout in earlier days, bewails the neglect of the age, and jestingly anticipates a day 'when the Scaligers and Daciers will vindicate my character, give learned editions of my labours, and bless the times, with copious comments on the text'. He then goes on to suppose 'one of your Chinese Owanowitzers, instructing one of your Tartarian Chinanobacchi' on the name and fame of Oliver Goldsmith. 'You see,' he remarks, 'I use Chinese names to show my own erudition, as I shall soon make our Chinese talk like an Englishman, to show his.' To all this, it need only be additionally stated, that Goldsmith's benefactor, Bishop Percy, had been lately engaged upon a Chinese novel.

The 'friend in the East', to whom Walpole's Chinese

Philosopher addressed his correspondence, was called Lien Chi; to find a name for his own Chinese philosopher in the Citizen of the World, Goldsmith merely added the cognomen Altangi. In respect of the setting and composition of the 'Chinese Letters', therefore, the two names which Goldsmith borrowed into his work, Zelis and Lien Chi, may well stand as symbols, the one, for the general influence of Montesquieu, the other, for such immediate and local influence as that of Horace Walpole and Bishop Percy.

The traveller-fable is a manner of writing at once easy and dangerous. If the writer be content to leave his foreign 'spy' a *voyageur abstrait*, the speaking picture of the author himself, without character or a national soul of his own, or if tie is to be a mere splenetic, peaking and puling at everything he sees, instead of a sane critic of life, then the traveller-fable is an easy style. The danger is, lest the 'spy' become an irresponsible cynic, lest his pen be driven more by 'peak', than by a healthy desire to discover the true colours of things. For there is no other style which permits to the fancy so loose a rein, and to the imagination so large a field of conceits, or which allows an exuberant and immature mind to run into wilder excesses. The traveller-fable has, of consequence, by this become so staled, that only one modern author of note has ever adventured with it.

Out of question, Goldsmith was put to some pains, in order to acquaint himself with so much of the Chinese national character and customs as would suffice to throw the proper amount of local colour into his work. That such local colour is only by starts correct, Leigh Hunt attributes 'to the barren and confused accounts of the Jesuit missionaries, and other prejudiced travellers, and to the want of an English embassy'; and he finds that, in the 'Chinese Letters', the demands of the traveller-fable were eminently fulfilled. In point of actual fact, China, in the Citizen of the World, is often only Utopia by another name. Goldsmith's authorities, Le Comte and Du Halde, were not faultless or entirely unprejudiced; nor did he himself here, more than in his 'Animated Nature', rest assured of every detail; and lastly, and above all, in this social map of his, he did not scruple to make his own samples, where they were actually wanting to fit his theme, just as, in the real geographical map, he fixed mountains and rivers where nature had not placed them, convenient to his purpose. For 'he was indeed, emphatically a popular writer. For accurate research or grave disquisition he was not well qualified by nature, or by education. He knew nothing accurately: his reading had been desultory; nor had he meditated deeply on what he had read.' So wrote Macaulay, in his oracular way; but of Oliver Goldsmith it was well and truly said, except that last clause, wherein there lies an unworthy sting and 'much offence'.

Leigh Hunt found that the chief merit of the Citizen of the World lay in the author's faculty to 'look beyond local and temporal absurdities; and, with that deeper insight, which regards a people's character, as it is influenced by popular habits and nationalities, to render the picture of their absurdities a lasting portrait', in which after ages may contemplate their features. A traveller who describes what he sees from the outside, is, to Goldsmith's mind, a vagabond. He must 'enter into the genius of nations', and, in his narration, must rather 'instruct the heart' of his reader, than 'indulge his imagination'.The extravagant fiction of Mandeville, who first in England brought the traveller's tale into just reproach, may well be said to have rather indulged the imagination than 'instructed the heart' of his readers; and Mandeville's antipodes, that 'raw boy', in Mackenzie's Man of Feeling, who 'arrived from the tour of Europe, with a Swiss valet for his companion, and half a dozen snuff-boxes with invisible hinges in his pocket', was a traveller who stopped short of 'entering into the genius' of nations : 'ask him of the manners of the people, and he will tell you that the skirt is worn much shorter in France, and that everybody eats macaroni in Italy'. Goldsmith's conception of the traveller-philosopher might well serve for an antidote to Mandeville, or to this 'raw boy' of

Mackenzie, or even to Sterne of the opposite extreme, with whom every event becomes an adventure, every incident starts a thought, seldom obvious or really reflective. All the heroes of the traveller-fable were philosophers, and Goldsmith was but moulding his work after a great model. He was also following the invariable practice of the Age of Reason: when, even in a fictive work like Rasselas, the critical and moral senses had the upper hand of the imagination; when the sage not often descended from the ethereal heights of philosophic abstraction; and when Nature herself, with all the witchery of sky and scene and sound, never found her way to the heart of the author, nor awaked any 'silent raptures' in his breast: to Dr. Johnson 'a blade of grass' was always a blade of grass 'whether in one country or another'.

And so in Goldsmith, where everything is frozen and made rigid with intellect, we could well spare some few pages of abstraction for a little more of the naive curiousness of Pepys, the faculty which Leigh Hunt would have coldly condemned as 'half-sighted observation'. Let the immortal Diary attest whether the lucubrations of this 'half-sighted' observer make not a more direct and lively appeal to the heart, than the speculations of an unschooled philosopher. That 'Journey to Kentish Town' will not be found the least interesting, though it was, perhaps, the most despised of the author's work, who labelled it scornfully enough: 'The manner of travellers, in their usual relations, ridiculed'. And I cannot forbear to wish that Goldsmith had indeed made that 'serious survey of the city wall' which he contemplated, 'when run dry on other topics', and enumerated 'the beauties of Shoe Lane'. 'There is one omission,' said Altangi, 'for which I expect no forgiveness: namely, my being totally silent upon their buildings, roads, rivers, and mountains'. It was ironically meant, for, after the creed of the rationalistic age, there was nothing to forgive.

But these general objections we can hardly forbear to recant, on a more intimate acquaintance with the work itself; seeing what excellent uses, in Goldsmith, philosophic abstraction serves. Since, then, it is with a philosopher that we have to do, and since we have already observed Goldsmith's prospect of the Republic of Letters, it will not be unfitting here to conclude these prefatory remarks with a rough scheme of his social and political doctrine.

As a practical politician, he discovered a democratic monarchy to be the most stable of all forms of government, and an absolute, the most powerful; but he judged it absurd that 'like children we should dress up puppets in finery, and then stand in astonishment at the plastic wonder'. Severity of laws increases the barbarity of peoples; the law should, like an indulgent parent, hold the rod, without chastising the child. With Horace Walpole, he finds that we have many 'names', without the corresponding 'ideas'; and frequently wonders that so many among us should be ready to offer up our lives for the mere sound, while so few are able to appreciate the real meaning of liberty. But national, and private Pride, and a fixed belief in his Liberty are the Englishman's chief prerogatives.

In Altangi's prospect of society, the betrayal of national partiality is never other than amusing; the ladies are 'horribly ugly', but as for the extravagances of wig, powder, and patch, the same follies have their rage, 'even among the Chinese': where national partiality would offend, the 'spy' is always an unprejudiced critic; English vanity he may wound; English national feeling, even in his censure, he respects. His social atmosphere is of the bourgeois and prosperous middle-class, of Vauxhall rather than Ranelagh. Though, like Elia, he may claim to feel for all indifferently, he cannot feel with all equally, nor 'like all people alike'; among the more pronounced of his imperfect sympathies are lawyers, doctors, the clergy, and the new sect called Methodists.

In this philosophical reasoning, the chief fault is that 'when mounted on the airy stilts of abstraction' his point of view is often deplorable; and that with him, as was remarked by Charles Lamb of an earlier casuist, the author of the Religio Medici, too often 'the possible takes the upper hand of the actual'. Thus, eloquently, and with an honest scepticism of orthodoxy, he reasons for a future consciousness: 'It must, it must surely be,' he cries, 'that this jarring, discordant life is but the prelude to some future harmony'; wherein he makes one grand omission, that a state of happiness is not an absolute, but a relative and subjective state. Real and practical social reform is impossible: the 'stilts' are built too high; his head is in the clouds; from such a height he cannot stoop to bow to social convention, to precedent, or necessity; 'the possible takes the upper hand of the actual'. So it is with his argument against kingship; he forgets that the grand necessity sanctions even the 'dressing of puppets': and it is this same ethereal abstraction, and contempt of the necessity of things, which makes him demur at the quoting of precedents in a lawsuit, and which allows him to confound the ragged banners in St Paul's, which are, after all, only the tattered symbols of national triumph, with the substantial rewards which 'this wise people fitted out a fleet and an army to seize'.

Goldsmith's commendation I have ushered in with an exception, at the same time honing that the faults in his philosophic system will not be thought to destroy that general sanity of view, which—whether in his reflections on the 'high' living of the clergy, on election extravagance, the epidemic terror and silly prepossessions of the people, on the Newmarket races, on London street-signs, ladies' head-dresses, or sentimental tragedy—in his prospect of society is everywhere displayed. Over the pages of no writer is just and obvious reflection sown with more careless prodigality than Goldsmith, no author is more remarkable for the unpremeditated and casual introduction of pregnant thought. The mind of the author comments on the meanest experiences of life, and leads him to reflections the most profound. He had gone to buy 'silk for a nightcap', and, the importunity of the shopman having persuaded him to the purchase of a waistcoat and a morning-gown, he cannot help reflecting that a man 'with such a confined education and capacity' could yet mould him to his purpose: 'the wisdom of the ignorant,' he profoundly remarks 'somewhat resembles the instinct of animals; it is diffused in but a very narrow sphere, but within that circle it acts with vigour, uniformity, and success'. From the same 'sentimental' source spring the kindred sensibilities of Goldsmith's nature, the reflective and the emotional. For to this sensibility to reflection on every accident of life, is allied that emotional sensibility, that sympathy and philanthropy, to which, with a splendid egoism, in his writings he so often confesses; and which has found for him a lasting place in the hearts of his countrymen, who love the man at least as much as they admire the author.

Apart from his humanity, it must, in the end, be confessed that the chief excellence of Goldsmith lies in his style; this, as an example of the height of perfection to which Augustan diction, with natural grace and classical elegance combined, can attain, has always been allowed unimpeachable. With all truth, it may be said of Goldsmith that he is uniformly pleasing; and this is higher praise than at first appears. The subjects of his thoughts are common, and his reflections, in general, obvious; but, in the prose of Goldsmith, common things assume a sort of epic dignity. With some writers, mental intensity, sounding the profoundest deeps of emotion and thought, will of itself inspire a soul into their language; with them, intrinsic vigour of mind is the very heart and essence of style. Such a writer Carlyle was; and such Ruskin is. A soul, bursting for utterance, will not be restrained within the fences of classicism. With Goldsmith, on the other hand, style is the conscious ornament of thought; and, garbed in the rich and graceful drapery of such language as his, the meanest thought, like a mean man surrounded with the circumstance of royalty, is enthroned with majesty and power.

The only objection which it seems reasonable to prefer against his style, is its want of emotional possibilities. Augustan prose, even of those writers who have attained such mastery of manner as Johnson and Goldsmith, is always unequal to the expression of the outbreak of passion; it never fails to satisfy the intellect, but seldom moves the heart. At the moment of its highest indignation, it rises with a gentle swell, and falls back, soothed by the sensuousness of its own harmony; it never breaks, like the prose of Carlyle, with a crash and a roar, against some rock of abuse, pitilessly hurling it to ruin: the deepest distress, on the other hand, nowhere inspires more than a few polite thrills of passion; emotion becomes sentiment merely. There is everywhere displayed a want of staccato power: in the smooth, harmonious tread of the classical period, there was no place for that irregular utterance, for those breaks and pauses of language, which are the visible concomitants of great sorrow. This failing is nowhere more evidenced than in the lamentations of Altangi over the desolation of his Chinese home, or those of Hingpo over the loss of his betrothed. Here we look in vain for that kind of speech, which, bursting the flood-gates of passion, pours upon the reader in a mighty resistless torrent, and overwhelms with an answering grief; or for that more mighty aposiopesis of sorrow, that pause and silence, which sickens with passion in restraint. This, however, while it constitutes a serious and glaring defect, is an objection to be urged rather against Augustan prose in general than the prose of any one author, like Goldsmith, in particular. After all, he was 'a very great man', and gloriously offended.

# Letters

# LETTER I

# A Character of the Chinese Philosopher

To Mr.
Merchant in London.
Amsterdam.

Sir,

Yours of the 13th instant, covering two bills, one on Messrs. R. and D., value £478, and the other on Mr. ———, value £285, duly came to hand; the former of which met with honour, but the other has been trifled with, and, I am afraid, will be returned protested.

The bearer of this is my friend, therefore let him be yours. He is a native of Honan in China, and one who did me signal services, when he was a mandarin, and I a factor, at Canton. By frequently conversing with the English there he has learned the language, though entirely a stranger to their manners and customs. I am told he is a philosopher; I am sure he is an honest man: that to you will be his best recommendation, next to the consideration of his being the friend of, Sir, Yours, &c.

P. L., Jan. 24, 1760.

# LETTER II

## Merchant in Amsterdam London

The Arrival Of The Chinese In London – His Motives For The Journey – Some Description Of The Streets And Houses.

From Lien Chi Altangi to Friend Of My Heart,

May the wings of peace rest upon thy dwelling, and the shield of conscience preserve thee from vice and misery! For all thy favours accept my gratitude and esteem, the only tributes a poor philosophic wanderer can return. Sure, fortune is resolved to make me unhappy, when she gives others a power of testifying their friendship by actions, and leaves me only words to express the sincerity of mine.

I am perfectly sensible of the delicacy, with which you to endeavour to lessen your own merit and my obligations. By calling your late instances of friendship only a return for former favours, you would induce me to impute to your justice what I owe to your generosity.

The services I did you at Canton, justice, humanity, and my office bade me perform; those you have done me since my arrival at Amsterdam, no laws obliged you to, no justice required.

Even half your favours would have been greater than my most sanguine expectations.

The sum of money, therefore, which you privately conveyed into my baggage, when I was leaving Holland, and which I was ignorant of till my arrival in London, I must beg leave to return. You have been bred a merchant, and I a scholar; you, consequently, love money better than I. You can find pleasure in superfluity; I am perfectly content with what is sufficient. Take, therefore, what is yours; it may give you some pleasure, even though you have no occasion to use it: my happiness it cannot improve, for I have already all that I want.

My passage by sea from Rotterdam to England was more painful to me, than all the journeys I ever made on land. I have traversed the immeasurable wilds of Mogul Tartary; felt alt the rigours of Siberian skies; I have had my repose a hundred times disturbed by invading savages, and have seen, without shrinking, the desert sands rise like a troubled ocean all around me. Against these calamities I was armed with resolution; but in my passage to England, though nothing occurred that gave the mariners any uneasiness, to one who was never at sea before, all was a subject of astonishment and terror. To find the land disappear, to see our ship mount the waves, swift as an arrow from the Tartar bow, to hear the wind howling through the cordage, to feel a sickness which depresses even the spirits of the brave; these were unexpected distresses, and consequently assaulted me, unprepared to receive them.

You men of Europe think nothing of a voyage by sea. With us of China, a man who has been from sight of land is regarded upon his return with admiration. I have known some provinces, where there is not even a name for the ocean. What a strange people, therefore, am I got amongst, who have founded an empire on this unstable element, who build cities upon billows that rise higher than the mountains of Tipartala, and make the deep more formidable than the wildest tempest!

Such accounts as these, I must confess, were my first motives for seeing England. These induced me to undertake a journey of seven hundred painful days, in order to examine its opulence, buildings, sciences, arts, and manufactures, on the spot. Judge, then, my disappointment on entering London, to see no signs of that opulence so much talked of abroad: wherever I turn I am presented with a gloomy solemnity in the houses, the streets, and the inhabitants; none of that beautiful gilding, which makes a principal ornament in Chinese architecture. The streets of Nankin are sometimes strewed with gold leaf; very different are those of London: in the midst of their pavement a great lazy puddle moves muddily along; heavy-laden machines, with wheels of unwieldy thickness, crowd up every passage; so that a stranger, instead of finding time for observation, is often happy if he has time to escape from being crushed to pieces.

The houses borrow very few ornaments from architecture; their chief decoration seems to be a paltry piece of painting hung out at their doors or windows, at once a proof of their indigence and vanity: their vanity, in each having one of those pictures exposed to public view; and their indigence, in being unable to get them better painted. In this respect the fancy of their painters is also deplorable. Could you believe it? I have seen five black lions and three blue boars in less than the circuit of half a mile; and yet you know that animals of these colours are nowhere to be found, except in the wild imaginations of Europe.

From these circumstances in their buildings, and from the dismal looks of the inhabitants, I am induced to conclude that the nation is actually poor; and that, like the Persians, they make a splendid figure everywhere but at home. The proverb of Xixofou is, that a man's riches may be seen in his eyes; if we judge of the English by this rule, there is not a poorer nation under the sun.

I have been here but two days, so will not be hasty in my decisions. Such letters as I shall write to Fipsihi in Moscow I beg you'll endeavour to forward with all diligence. I shall send them open, in order that you may take copies or translations, as you are equally versed in the Dutch and Chinese languages. Dear friend, think of my absence with regret, as I sincerely regret yours; even while I write, I lament our separation. Farewell.

P. L., Jan. 24, 1760.

# LETTER III

## The Description Of London Continued
## - The Luxury Of The English - Its Benefits
## - The Fine Gentleman - The Fine Lady

From Lien Chi Altangi to the care of Fipsihi, resident in Moscow, to be forwarded by the Russian caravan to Fum Hoam, First President of the Ceremonial Academy at Pekin, in China.

Think not, O thou guide of my youth, that absence can impair my respect, or interposing trackless deserts blot your reverend figure from my memory. The farther I travel, I feel the pain of separation with stronger force; those ties that bind me to my native country and you are still unbroken. By every remove I only drag a greater length of chain.

Could I find ought worth transmitting from so remote a region, as this to which I have wandered, I should gladly send it; but, instead of this, you must be content with a renewal of my former professions, and an imperfect account of a people, with whom I am as yet but superficially acquainted. The remarks of a man, who has been but three days in the country, can only be those obvious circumstances, which force themselves upon the imagination. I consider myself here as a newly created being introduced into a new world. Every object strikes with wonder and surprise. The imagination, still unsated, seems the only active principle of the mind. The most trifling occurrences give pleasure, till the gloss of novelty is worn away. When I have ceased to wonder, I may possibly grow wise; I may then call the reasoning principle to my aid, and compare those objects with each other, which were before examined without reflection.

Behold me, then, in London, gazing at the strangers and they at me. It seems they find somewhat absurd in my figure; and, had I never been from home, it is possible I might find an infinite fund of ridicule in theirs: but by long travelling I am taught to laugh at folly alone, and to find nothing truly ridiculous but villainy and vice.

When I had just quitted my native country, and crossed the Chinese wall, I fancied every deviation from the customs and manners of China was a departing from nature. I smiled at the blue lips and red foreheads of the Tonguese; and could hardly contain when I saw the Daures dress their heads with horns: the Ostiacs powdered with red earth and the Calmuck beauties, tricked out in all the finery of sheepskin, appeared highly ridiculous. But I soon perceived that the ridicule lay not in them, but in me; that I falsely condemned others for absurdity, because they happened to differ from a standard so originally founded in prejudice or partiality.

I find no pleasure, therefore, in taxing the English with departing from nature in their external appearance, which is all I yet know of their character: it is possible they only endeavour to improve her simple plan, since every extravagance in dress proceeds from a desire of becoming more beautiful than nature made us; and this is so harmless a vanity, that I not only pardon, but approve it. A desire to be more excellent than others is what actually makes us so; and, as thousands find a livelihood in society by such appetites, none but the ignorant inveigh against them.

You are not insensible, most reverend Fum Hoam, what numberless trades, even among the Chinese, subsist by the harmless pride of each other. Your nose-borers, feet-swathers, teeth-stain-ers, eyebrow-pluckers, would all want bread, should their neigh-bours want vanity. These vanities, however, employ much fewer hands in China than in England; and a fine gentleman or a fine lady here, dressed up to the fashion, seems scarcely to have a single limb that does not suffer some distortions from art.

To make a fine gentleman, several trades are required, but chiefly a barber. You have undoubtedly heard of the Jewish champion, whose strength lay in his hair; one would think that the English were for placing all wisdom there: to appear wise, nothing more is requisite here, than for a man to borrow hair from the heads of all his neighbours, and clap it like a bush on his own. The distributors of law and physic stick on such quantities, that it is almost impossible, even in idea, to distinguish between the head and the hair.

Those whom I have now been describing affect the gravity of the lion; those I am going to describe more resemble the pert vivacity of smaller animals. The barber, who is still master of the ceremonies, cuts their hair close to the crown; and then, with a composition of meal and hog's-lard, plasters the whole in such a manner as to make it impossible to distinguish whether the patient wears a cap or a plaster; but, to make the picture more perfectly striking, conceive the tail of some beast, a grey-hound's tail, or a pig's tail, for instance, appended to the back of the head. Thus betailed and bepowdered, the man of taste fancies he improves in beauty, dresses up his hard-featured face in smiles, and attempts to look hideously tender. Thus equipped, he is qualified to make love, and hopes for success more from the powder on the outside of his head than the sentiments within.

Yet when I consider what sort of a creature the fine lady is, to whom he is supposed to pay his addresses, it is not strange to find him thus equipped in order to please. She is herself every whit as fond of powder, and tails, and hog's-lard, as he. To speak my secret sentiments, most reverend Fum, the ladies here are horribly ugly; I can hardly endure the sight of them; they no way resemble the beauties of China: the Europeans have a quite different idea of beauty from us. When I reflect on the small-footed perfections of an Eastern beauty, how is it possible I should have eyes for a woman whose feet are ten inches long? I shall never forget the beauties of my native city of Nangfew. How very broad their faces! How very short their noses! How very little their eyes! How very thin their lips! How very black their teeth! The snow on the tops of Bao is not fairer than their cheeks; and their eyebrows are small as the line by the pencil of Quamsi. Here a lady with such perfections would be frightful. Dutch and Chinese beauties, indeed, have some resemblance, but English women are entirely different: red cheeks, big eyes, and teeth of a most odious whiteness, are not only seen here, but wished for; and then they have such masculine feet, as actually serve some for walking!

Yet, uncivil as nature has been, they seem resolved to outdo her in unkindness: they use white powder, blue powder, and black powder for their hair, and a red powder for the face on some particular occasions. They like to have the face of various colours, as among the Tartars of Koreki, frequently sticking on, with spittle, little black patches on every part of it, except on the tip of the nose, which I have never seen with a patch. You'll have a better idea of their manner of placing these spots, when I have finished a map of an English face, patched up to the fashion, which shall shortly be sent, to increase your curious collection of paintings, medals, and monsters.

But what surprises more than all the rest is what I have just now been credibly informed of by one of this country. 'Most ladies here', says he, 'have two faces: one face to sleep in, and another to show in company. The first is generally reserved for the husband and family at home; the other put on to please strangers abroad: the family face is often indifferent enough, but the out-door one looks something better; this is always made at the toilet, where the looking-glass and toad-eater sit in council, and settle the complexion of the day.'

I cannot ascertain the truth of this remark. However, it is actually certain, that they wear more clothes within doors than without; and I have seen a lady, who seemed to shudder at a breeze in her own apartment, appear half naked in the streets. Farewell.

P. L., Jan. 29, 1760.

# LETTER IV

## English Pride – Liberty - An Instance Of Both – Newspapers - Politeness

To the same.

The English seem as silent as the Japanese, yet vainer than the inhabitants of Siam. Upon my arrival, I attributed that reserve to modesty, which, I now find, has its origin in pride. Condescend to address them first, and you are sure of their acquaintance; stoop to flattery, and you conciliate their friendship, and esteem. They bear hunger, cold, fatigue, and all the miseries of life, without shrinking; danger only calls forth their fortitude; they even exult in calamity: but contempt is what they cannot bear. An Englishman fears contempt more than death; he often flies to death as a refuge from its pressure; and dies, when he fancies the world has ceased to esteem him.

Pride seems the source not only of their national vices, but of their national virtues also. An Englishman is taught to love his king as his friend, but to acknowledge no other master than the laws, which himself has contributed to enact. He despises those nations who, that one may be free, are all content to be slaves; who first lift a tyrant into terror, and then shrink under his power, as if delegated from Heaven. Liberty is echoed in all their assemblies; and thousands might be found ready to offer up their lives for the sound, though perhaps not one of all the number understands its meaning. The lowest mechanic, however, looks upon it as his duty to be a watchful guardian of his country's freedom, and often uses a language, that might seem haughty, even in the mouth of the great emperor, who traces his ancestry to the Moon.

A few days ago, passing by one of their prisons, I could not avoid stopping, in order to listen to a dialogue, which, I thought, might afford me some entertainment. The conversation was carried on between a debtor, through the grate of his prison, a porter, who had stopped to rest his burden, and a soldier, at the window. The subject was upon a threatened invasion from France, and each seemed extremely anxious to rescue his country from the impending danger.

'For my part,' cries the prisoner, 'the greatest of my apprehensions is for our freedom; if the French should conquer, what would become of English liberty? My dear friends, liberty is the Englishman's prerogative; we must preserve that, at the expense of our lives; of that the French shall never deprive us. It is not to be expected that men, who are slaves themselves, would preserve our freedom, should they happen to conquer.' 'Ay, slaves,' cries the porter, 'they are all slaves, fit only to carry burdens, every one of them. Before I would stoop to slavery, may this be my poison! (and he held the goblet in his hands) may this be my poison!— but I would sooner list for a soldier.'

The soldier, taking the goblet from his friend with much awe, fervently cried out: 'It is not so much our liberties, as our religion, that would suffer by such a change; ay, our religion, my lads. May the devil sink me into flames, (such was the solemnity of his adjuration) if the French should come over, but our religion would be utterly undone!' So saying, instead of a libation, he applied the goblet to his lips, and confirmed his sentiments with a ceremony of the most persevering devotion.

In short, every man here pretends to be a politician; even the fair sex are sometimes found to mix the severity of national altercation with the blandishments of love, and often become conquerors by more weapons of destruction than their eyes.

This universal passion for politics is gratified by daily gazettes, as with us in China. But, as in ours the emperor endeavours to instruct his people, in theirs, the people endeavour to instruct the administration. You must not, however, imagine that they who compile these papers have any actual knowledge of the politics, or the government, of a state: they only collect their materials from the oracle of some coffee-house, which oracle has himself gathered them, the night before, from a beau at a gaming-table, who has pillaged his knowledge from a great man's porter, who has had his information from the great man's gentleman, who has invented the whole story for his own amusement, the night preceding.

The English, in general, seem fonder of gaining the esteem, than the love, of those they converse with. This gives a formality to their amusements; their gayest conversations have something too wise for innocent relaxation: though in company you are seldom disgusted with the absurdity of a fool, you are seldom lifted into rapture by those strokes of vivacity, which give instant, though not permanent, pleasure.

What they want, however, in gaiety, they make up in politeness. You smile at hearing me praise the English for their politeness; you, who have heard very different accounts from the missionaries at Pekin, who have seen such a different behaviour in their merchants and seamen at home. But, I must still repeat it, the English seem more polite than any of their neighbours; their great art in this respect lies in endeavouring, while they oblige, to lessen the force of the favour. Other countries are fond of obliging a stranger; but seem desirous that he should be sensible of the obligation, the English confer their kindness with an appearance of indifference, and give away benefits with an air as if they despised them.

Walking, a few days ago, between an English and a French man into the suburbs of the city, we were overtaken by a heavy shower of rain. I was unprepared; but they had each large coats, which defended them from what seemed to me a perfect inundation. The Englishman, seeing me shrink from the weather, accosted me thus: 'Psha, man, what dost shrink at? Here, take this coat; I don't want it; I find it no way useful to me; I had as lief be without it.' The Frenchman' began to show his politeness in turn. 'My dear friend,' cries he, 'why won't you oblige me by making use of my coat? You see how well it defends me from the rain; I should not choose to part with it to others, but, to such a friend as you, I could even part with my skin to do him service.'

From such minute instances as these, most reverend Fum Hoam, I am sensible your sagacity will collect instruction. The volume of nature is the book of knowledge; and he becomes most wise, who makes the most judicious selection. Farewell.

P. L., Jan. 31, 1760.

# LETTER V

## Happiness Lost By Seeking After Refinement - The Chinese Philosopher's Disgraces

Fum Hoam, First President of the Ceremonial Academy at Pekin, to Lien Chi Altangi, the discontented Wanderer; by the way of Moscow.

Whether sporting on the flowery banks of the river Irtis, or scaling the sleepy mountains of Douchenour; whether traversing the black deserts of Kobi, or giving lessons of politeness to the savage inhabitants of Europe; in whatever country, whatever climate, and whatever circumstances, all hail! May Tien, the Universal Soul, take you under his protection, and inspire you with a superior portion of himself!

How long, my friend, shall an enthusiasm for knowledge continue to obstruct your happiness, and tear you from all the connexions that make life pleasing? How long will you continue to rove from climate to climate, circled by thousands, and yet without a friend, feeling all the inconveniences of a crowd, and all the anxiety of being alone?

I know you will reply that the refined pleasure of growing every day wiser is a sufficient recompense for every inconvenience. I know you will talk of the vulgar satisfaction of soliciting happiness from sensual enjoyment only; and probably enlarge upon the exquisite raptures of sentimental bliss. Yet, believe me, friend, you are deceived; all our pleasures, though seemingly never so remote from sense, derive their origin from some one of the senses. The most exquisite demonstration in mathematics, or the most pleasing disquisition in metaphysics, if it does not ultimately tend to increase some sensual satisfaction, is delightful only to fools, or to men who have, by long habit, contracted a false idea of pleasure; and he who separates sensual and sentimental enjoyments, seeking happiness from mind alone, is, in fact, as wretched as the naked inhabitant of the forest, who places all happiness in the first, regardless of the latter. There are two extremes in this respect: the savage, who swallows down the draught of pleasure, without staying to reflect on his happiness; and the sage, who passeth the cup, while he reflects on the conveniences of drinking.

It is with an heart full of sorrow, my dear Altangi, that I must inform you, that what the world calls happiness must now be yours no longer. Our great emperor's displeasure at your leaving China, contrary to the rules of our government, and the immemorial custom of the empire, has produced the most terrible effects. Your wife, daughter, and the rest of your family, have been seized by his order, and appropriated to his use; all, except your son, are now the peculiar property of him who possesses all: him I have hidden from the officers employed for this pose; and, even at the hazard of my life, I have concealed him. The youth seems obstinately bent on finding you out, wherever you are; he is determined to face every danger that opposes his pursuit. Though yet but fifteen, all his father's virtues and obstinacy sparkle in his eyes, and mark him as one destined to no mediocrity of fortune.

You see, my dearest friend, what imprudence has brought thee to: from opulence, a tender family, surrounding friends, and your master's esteem, it has reduced thee to want, persecution, and, still worse, to our mighty monarch's displeasure. Want of prudence is too frequently the want of virtue; nor is there on earth a more powerful advocate for vice than poverty. As I shall endeavour to guard thee from the one, so guard thyself from the other; and still think of me with affection and esteem. Farewell.

# LETTER VI

## The Journey Of The Chinese
## From Pekin To Moscow - The
## Customs Of The Daures

From Lien Chi Altangi to Film Hoam, First President of the
Ceremonial Academy at Pekin, in China.

I have hitherto given you no account of my journey from
China to Europe, of my travels through countries, where nature
sports in primeval rudeness, where she pours forth her wonders in solitude; countries, from whence the rigorous climate,
the sweeping inundation, the drifted desert, the howling forest,
and mountains of immeasurable height banish the husbandman,
and spread extensive desolation; countries, where the brown
Tartar wanders for a precarious subsistence, with an heart
that never felt pity, himself more hideous than the wilderness
he makes.

You will easily conceive the fatigue of crossing vast tracts of
land, either desolate, or still more dangerous by its inhabitants
the retreat of men, who seem driven from society, in order to
make war upon all the human race; nominally professing a
subjection to Muscovy or China, but without any resemblance
to the countries, on which they depend.

After I had crossed the Great Wall, the first objects that presented themselves were the remains of desolated cities, and all the magnificence of venerable ruin. There were to be seen temples of beautiful structure, statues wrought by the hand of a master, and around, a country of luxuriant plenty; but not one single inhabitant to reap the bounties of nature. These were prospects that might humble the pride of kings, and repress human vanity. I asked my guide the cause of such desolation. These countries, says he, were once the dominions of a Tartar prince; and these ruins, the seat of arts, elegance, and ease. This prince waged an unsuccessful war with one of the emperors of China; he was conquered, his cities plundered, and all his subjects carried into captivity. Such are the effects of the ambition of kings! Ten dervises, says the Indian proverb, shall sleep in peace upon a single carpet, while two kings shall quarrel, though they have kingdoms to divide them. Sure, my friend, the cruelty and the pride of man have made more deserts, than Nature ever made; she is kind, but man is ungrateful!

Proceeding in my journey through this pensive scene of desolated beauty, in a few days I arrived among the Pautes, a nation still dependent on China. Xaizigar is their principal city, which, compared with those of Europe, scarcely deserves the name. The governors, and other officers, who are sent yearly from Pekin, abuse their authority, and often take the wives and daughters of the inhabitants to themselves. The Daures, accustomed to base submission, feel no resentment at these injuries, or stifle what they feel. Custom and necessity teach even barbarians the same art of dissimulation, that ambition and intrigue inspire in the breasts of the polite. Upon beholding such unlicensed stretches of power, alas, thought I, how little does our wise and good emperor know of these intolerable exactions! These provinces are too distant for complaint, and too insignificant to expect redress. The more distant the government, the honester should be the governor, to whom it is entrusted; for hope of impunity is a strong inducement to violation.

The religion of the Daures is more absurd, than even that of the sectaries of Fohi. How would you be surprised, O sage disciple and follower of Confucius, you, who believe one eternal intelligent cause of all, should you be present at the barbarous ceremonies of this infatuated people! How would you deplore the blindness and folly of mankind! His boasted reason seems only to light him astray, and brutal instinct more regularly points out the path to happiness. Could you think it? They adore a wicked divinity; they fear him, and they worship him; they imagine him a malicious Being, ready to injure, and ready to be appeased. The men and women assemble at midnight in a hut, which serves for a temple. A priest stretches himself on the ground, and all the people pour forth the most horrid cries, while drums and timbrels swell the infernal concert. After this dissonance, miscalled music, has continued about two hours, the priest rises from the ground, assumes an air of inspiration, grows big with the inspiring daemon, and pretends to a skill in futurity.

In every country, my friend, the bonzes, the brahmins, and the priests deceive the people: all reformations begin from the laity; the priests point us out the way to heaven with their fingers, but stand still themselves, nor seem to travel towards the country in view.

The customs of this people correspond to their religion: they keep their dead for three days on the same bed where the person died; after which they bury him in a grave moderately deep, but with the head still uncovered. Here for several days they present him different sorts of meats; which, when they perceive he does not consume, they fill up the grave, and desist from desiring him to eat for the future. How, how can mankind be guilty of such strange absurdity? To entreat a dead body, already putrid, to partake of the banquet! Where, I again repeat it, is human reason? Not only some men, but whole nations, seem divested of its illumination. Here we observe a whole country adoring a divinity through fear, and attempting to feed the dead. These are their most serious, and most religious occupations. Are these men rational, or are not the apes of Borneo more wise?

Certain I am, O thou instructor of my youth, that, without philosophers, without some few virtuous men, who seem to be of a different nature from the rest of mankind, without such as these, the worship of a wicked divinity would surely be established over every part of the earth. Fear guides more to their, duty than gratitude: for one man, who is virtuous from the love of virtue, from the obligation, which he thinks he lies under to the Giver of all, there are ten thousand, who are good only from their apprehensions of punishment. Could these last be persuaded, as the Epicureans were, that heaven had no thunders in store for the villain, they would no longer continue to acknowledge subordination, or thank that Being, who gave them existence. Adieu.

P. L., Feb. 14, 1760.

# LETTER VII

## An Account Of Westminster Abbey

To the same.

I am just returned from Westminster Abbey, the place of sepul-
ture for the philosophers, heroes, and kings of England. What
a gloom do monumental inscriptions, and all the venerable
remains of deceased merit inspire! Imagine a temple, marked
with the hand of antiquity, o solemn as religious awe, adorned
with all the magnificence of barbarous profusion, dim windows,
fretted pillars, long colonnades, and dark ceilings. Think, then,
what were my sensations at being introduced to such a scene
I stood in the midst of the temple, and threw my eyes round
on the walls, filled with the statues, the inscriptions, and the
monuments, of the dead.

Alas, I said to myself, how does pride attend the puny child
of dust even to the grave! Even humble as I am, I possess more
consequence in the present scene, than the greatest hero of them
all; they have toiled for an hour to gain a transient immortality, and are at length retired to the grave, where they have no
attendant but the worm, none to flatter but the epitaph.

As I was indulging such reflections, a gentleman dressed in black, perceiving me to be a stranger, came up, entered into conversation, and politely offered to be my instructor and guide through the temple.

'If any monument', said he, 'should particularly excite your curiosity, I shall endeavour to satisfy your demands.'

I accepted, with thanks, the gentleman's offer, adding that 'I was come to observe the policy, the wisdom, and the justice of the English, in conferring rewards upon deceased merit'.

'If adulation like this', continued I, 'be properly conducted, as it can no ways injure those, who are flattered, so it may be a glorious incentive to those, who are now capable of enjoying it. It is the duty of every good government to turn this monumental pride to its own advantage; to become strong in the aggregate from the weakness of the individual. If none but the truly great have a place in this awful repository, a temple like this will give the finest lessons of morality, and be a strong incentive to true ambition. I am told, that none have a place here, but characters of the most distinguished merit.'

The Man in Black seemed impatient at my observations; so I discontinued my remarks, and we walked on together, to take a view of every particular monument in order as it lay.

As the eye is naturally caught by the finest objects, I could not avoid being particularly curious about one monument, which appeared more beautiful than the rest.

'That', said I to my guide, 'I take to be the tomb of some very great man. By the peculiar excellence of the workmanship, and the magnificence of the design, this must be a trophy raised to the memory of some king, who has saved his country from ruin, or lawgiver, who has reduced his fellow-citizens from anarchy into just subjection.'

'It is not requisite', replied my companion, smiling, '•to have such qualifications, in order to have a very fine monument here; more humble abilities will suffice.'

'What! I suppose, then, the gaining two or three battles, or

64

the taking half a score of towns, is thought a sufficient quali-
fication?'

'Gaining battles, or taking towns,' replied the Man in Black,
'may be of service; but a gentleman may have a very fine monument here, without ever seeing a battle or a siege.'

'This, then, is the monument of some poet, I presume, of one
whose wit has gained him immortality?'

'No, sir,' replied my guide, 'the gentleman who lies here never
made verses; and, as for wit, he despised it in others, because he
had none himself.'

'Pray tell me, then, in a word,' said I, peevishly, 'what is the
great man who lies here particularly remarkable for?'

'Remarkable, sir,' said my companion; 'why, sir, the gentleman that lies here is remarkable, very remarkable, for a tomb in
Westminster Abbey.'

'But, head of my ancestors, how has he got here? I fancy he
could never bribe the guardians of the temple to give him a
place. Should he not be ashamed to be seen among company,
where even moderate merit would look like infamy?'

'I suppose', replied the Man in Black, 'the gentleman was rich,
and his friends, as is usual in such a case, told him he was great.
He readily believed them; the guardians of the temple, as they
got by the self-delusion, were ready to believe him too; so he
paid his money for a fine monument; and the workman, as you
see, has made him one of the most beautiful. Think not, however, that this gentleman is singular in his desire of being buried
among the great; there are several others in the temple, who,
hated and shunned by the great, while alive, have come here
fully resolved to keep them company, now they are dead.'

As we walked along to a particular part of the temple, 'There,'
says the gentleman, pointing with his finger, 'that is the Poets'
Corner; there you see the monuments of Shakespeare, and
Milton, and Prior, and Drayton.'

'Drayton!' I replied; 'I never heard of him before; but I have
been told of one Pope; is he there?'

'It is time enough,' replied my guide, 'these hundred years; he is not long dead; people have not done hating him yet.'

'Strange,' cried I; 'can any be found to hate a man, whose life was wholly spent in entertaining and instructing his fellow-creatures?'

'Yes,' says my guide, 'they hate him for that very reason. There are a set of men called answerers of books, who take upon them to watch the republic of letters, and distribute reputation by the sheet; they somewhat resemble eunuchs in a seraglio, who are incapable of giving pleasure themselves, and hinder those that would. These answerers have no other employment but to cry out Dunce and Scribbler; to praise the dead, and revile the living; to so grant a man of confessed abilities some small share of merit; to applaud twenty blockheads, in order to gain the reputation of candour; and to revile the moral character of the man, whose writings they cannot injure. Such wretches are kept in pay by some mercenary bookseller, or more frequently the bookseller himself takes this dirty work off their hands, as all that is required is to be very abusive and very dull. Every poet of any genius is sure to find such enemies; he feels, though he seems to despise, their malice; they make him miserable here, and, in the pursuit of empty fame, at last he gains solid anxiety.'

'Has this been the case with every poet I see here?' cried I.

'Yes, with every mother's son of them,' replied he, 'except he happened to be born a mandarin. If he has much money, he may buy reputation from your book-answerers, as well as a monument from the guardians of the temple.'

'But are there not some men of distinguished taste, as in China, who are willing to patronize men of merit, and soften the rancour of malevolent dulness?'

'I own there are many,' replied the Man in Black; 'but, alas, sir, the book-answerers crowd about them, and call themselves the writers of books; and the patron is too indolent to distinguish: thus poets are kept at a distance, while their enemies eat up all their rewards at the mandarin's table.'

Leaving this part of the temple, we made up to an iron gate, through which my companion told me we were to pass, in order to see the monuments of the kings. Accordingly, I marched up without further ceremony, and was going to enter, when a person, who held the gate in his hand, told me I must pay first. I was surprised at such a demand; and asked the man, whether the people of England kept a show; whether the paltry sum he demanded was not a national reproach; whether it was not more to the honour of the country to let their magnificence or their antiquities be openly seen, than thus meanly to tax a curiosity, which tended to their own honour.

'As for your questions,' replied the gate-keeper, 'to be sure they may be very right, because I don't understand them; but, as for that there threepence, I farm it from one, who rents it from another, who hires it from a third, who leases it from the guardians of the temple: and we all must live.'

I expected, upon paying here, to see something extraordinary, since what I had seen for nothing filled me with so much surprise: but in this I was disappointed; there was little more within than black coffins, rusty armour, tattered standards, and some few slovenly figures in wax. I was sorry I had paid, but I comforted myself by considering it would be my last payment. A person attended us who, without once blushing, told an hundred lies: he told of a lady who died by pricking her finger; of a king with a golden head, and twenty such pieces of absurdity.

'Look ye there, gentlemen,' says he, pointing to an old oak chair, 'there's a curiosity for ye; in that chair the kings of England were crowned: you see also a stone underneath, and that stone is Jacob's pillow.'

I could see no curiosity either in the oak chair or the stone: could I, indeed, behold one of the old kings of England seated in this, or Jacob's head laid upon the other, there might be something curious in the sight; but, in the present case, there was no more reason for my surprise, than if I should pick a stone from their streets, and call it a curiosity, merely because one of the kings happened to tread upon it as he passed in a procession.

From hence our conductor led us through several dark walks and winding ways, uttering lies, talking to himself, so and flourishing a wand, which he held in his hand. He reminded me of the black magicians of Kobi. After we had been almost fatigued with a variety of objects, he at last desired me to consider attentively a certain suit of armour, which seemed to show nothing remarkable.

'This armour', said he, 'belonged to General Monk.'

'Very surprising that a general should wear armour!'

'And pray,' added he, 'observe this cap; this is General Monk's cap.'

'Very strange indeed, very strange, that a general should have a cap also! Pray, friend, what might this cap have cost originally?'

'That, sir,' says he, 'I don't know; but this cap is all the wages I have for my trouble.'

'A very small recompense, truly,' said I.

'Not so very small,' replied he, 'for every gentleman ruts some money into it, and I spend the money.'

'What, more money, still more money!'

'Every gentleman gives something, sir.'

'I'll give thee nothing,' returned I; 'the guardians of the temple should pay you your wages, friend, and not permit you to squeeze thus from every spectator. When we pay our money at the door to see a show, we never give more, as we are going out. Sure, the guardians of so the temple can never think they get enough. Show me the gate; if I stay longer, I may probably meet with more of those ecclesiastical beggars.'

Thus leaving the temple precipitately, I returned to my lodgings, in order to ruminate over what was great, and to despise what was mean, in the occurrences of the day.

P. L., Feb. 25, 1760.

# LETTER VIII

## The Chinese Goes To See A Play

To the same.

The English are as fond of seeing plays acted as the Chinese; but there is a vast difference in the manner of conducting them. We play our pieces in the open air, the English theirs under cover; we act by daylight, they by the blaze of torches. One of our plays continues eight or ten days successively; an English piece seldom takes up above four hours in the representation.

My companion in black, with whom I am now beginning to contract an intimacy, introduced me a few nights ago to the play-house, where we placed ourselves conveniently at the foot of the stage. As the curtain was not drawn before my arrival, I had an opportunity of observing the behaviour of the spectators, and indulging those reflections, which novelty generally inspires.

The richest in general were placed in the lowest seats, and the poor rose above them in degrees proportioned to their poverty. The order of precedence seemed here inverted: those, who were undermost all the day, now enjoyed a temporary eminence, and became masters of the ceremonies. It was they who called for the music, indulging every noisy freedom, and testifying all the insolence of beggary in exaltation.

They who held the middle region seemed not so riotous as those above them, nor yet so tame as those below: to judge by their looks, many of them seemed strangers there as well as myself; they were chiefly employed, during this period of expectation, in eating oranges, reading the story of the play, or making assignations.

Those who sat in the lowest rows, which are called the pit, seemed to consider themselves as judges of the merit of the poet and the performers: they were assembled partly to be amused, and partly to show their taste; appearing to labour under that restraint, which an affectation of superior discernment generally produces. My companion, however, informed me, that not one in a hundred of them knew even the first principles of criticism; that they assumed the right of being censors, because there was none to contradict their pretensions; and that every man, who now called himself a connoisseur, became such to all intents and purposes.

Those who sat in the boxes appeared in the most unhappy situation of all. The rest of the audience came merely for their own amusement; these, rather to furnish out a part of the entertainment themselves. I could not avoid considering them as acting parts in dumb show; not a curtsey or nod, that was not the result of art; not a look nor a smile, that was not designed for murder. Gentlemen and ladies ogled each other through spectacles; for my companion observed, that blindness was of late become fashionable; all affected indifference and ease, while their hearts at the same time burned for conquest. Upon the whole, the lights, the music, the ladies in their gayest dresses, the men with cheerfulness and expectation in their looks, all conspired to make a most agreeable picture, and to fill a heart, that sympathises at human happiness, with inexpressible serenity.

The expected time for the play to begin at last arrived; the curtain was drawn, and the actors came on. A woman, who personated a queen, came in curtseying to the audience, who clapped their hands upon her appearance. Clapping of hands is, it seems, the manner of applauding in England; the manner is absurd, but every country, you know, has its peculiar absurdities. I was equally surprised, however, at the submission of the actress, who should have considered herself as a queen, as at the little discernment of the audience, who gave her such marks of applause, before she attempted to deserve them. Preliminaries between her and the audience being thus adjusted, the dialogue was supported between her and a most hopeful youth, who acted the part of her confidant. They both appeared in extreme distress, for it seems the queen had lost a child some fifteen years before, and still kept its dear resemblance next her heart, while her kind companion bore a part in her sorrows.

Her lamentations grew loud; comfort is offered, but she detests the very sound: she bids them preach comfort to the winds. Upon this her husband comes in, who, seeing the queen so much afflicted, can himself hardly refrain from tears, or avoid partaking in the soft distress. After thus grieving through three scenes, the curtain dropped for the first act.

'Truly,' said I to my companion, 'these kings and queens are very much disturbed at no very great misfortune; certain I am, were people of humbler stations to act in this manner, they would be thought divested of common sense.'

I had scarce finished this observation, when the curtain rose, and the king came on in a violent passion. His wife had, it seems, refused his proffered tenderness, had spurned his royal embrace; and he seemed resolved not to survive her fierce disdain. After he had thus fretted, and the queen had fretted, through the second act, the curtain was let down once more.

'Now,' says my companion, 'you perceive the king to be a man of spirit; he feels at every pore: one of your phlegmatic sons of clay would have given the queen her own way, and let her come to herself by degrees; but the king is for immediate tenderness, or instant death: death and tenderness are leading passions of every modern buskined hero; this moment they embrace, and the next stab, mixing daggers and kisses in every period.'

I was going to second his remarks, when my attention so was engrossed by a new object: a man came in, balancing a straw upon his nose, and the audience were clapping their hands in all the raptures of applause.

'To what purpose,' cried I, 'does this unmeaning figure make his appearance? Is he a part of the plot?'

'Unmeaning do you call him?' replied my friend in black; 'this is one of the most important characters of the whole play; nothing pleases the people more, than the seeing a straw balanced: there is a great deal of meaning in a straw: there is something suited to every apprehension in the sight; and a fellow possessed of talents like these is sure of making his fortune.'

The third act now began with an actor, who came to inform us that he was the villain of the play, and intended to show strange things, before all was over. He was joined by another, who seemed as much disposed for mischief as he; their intrigues continued through this whole division.

'If that be a villain,' said I, 'he must be a very stupid one, to tell his secrets without being asked; such soliloquies of late are never admitted in China.'

The noise of clapping interrupted me once more; a child of six years old was learning to dance on the stage, which gave the ladies and mandarins infinite satisfaction.

'I am sorry', said I, 'to see the pretty creature so early learning so bad a trade; dancing being, I presume, as contemptible here, as it is in China.'

'Quite the reverse,' interrupted my companion; 'dancing is a very reputable and genteel employment here; men have a greater chance for encouragement from the merit of their heels, than their heads. One who jumps up, and flourishes his toes three times, before he comes to the ground, may have three hundred a year: he, who flourishes them four times, gets four hundred; but he who arrives at five is inestimable, and may demand what salary he thinks proper. The female dancers, too, are valued for this sort of jumping and crossing. But the fourth act is begun; let us be attentive.'

In the fourth act, the queen finds her long-lost child, now grown up into a youth of smart parts and great qualifications; wherefore she wisely considers that the crown will fit his head better than that of her husband, whom she knows to be a driveller. The king discovers her design, and here comes on the deep distress; he loves the queen, and he loves the kingdom; he resolves, therefore, in order to possess both, that her son must die. The queen exclaims at his barbarity, is frantic with rage, and, at length, overcome with sorrow, falls into a fit; upon which the curtain drops, and the act is concluded.

'Observe the art of the poet,' cries my companion. 'When the queen can say no more, she falls into a fit. While thus her eyes are shut, while she is supported in the arms of her Abigail, what horrors do we not fancy! We feel it in every nerve; take my word for it, that fits are the true aposiopesis of modern tragedy.'

The fifth act began, and a busy piece it was. Scenes shifting, trumpets sounding, mobs hallooing, carpets spreading, guards bustling from one door to another; gods, demons, daggers, racks, and ratsbane. But whether the king was killed, or the queen was drowned, or the son was poisoned, I have absolutely forgotten.

When the play was over, I could not avoid observing, that the persons of the drama appeared in as much distress in the first act, as the last.

'How is it possible,' said I, 'to sympathise with them through five long acts! Pity is but a short-lived passion. I hate to hear an actor mouthing trifles: neither startings, strainings, nor attitudes affect me, unless there be cause; after I have been once or twice deceived by those unmeaning alarms, my heart sleeps in peace, probably unaffected by the principal distress. There should be one great passion aimed at by the actor, as well as the poet; all the rest should be subordinate, and only contribute to make that the greater: if the actor, therefore, exclaims upon every occasion, in tones of despair, he attempts to move us too soon; he anticipates the blow; he ceases to affect, though he gains our applause.'

I scarce perceived that the audience were almost all departed; wherefore, mixing with the crowd, my companion and I got into the street; where, essaying an hundred obstacles from coach-wheels and palanquin poles, like birds in their flight through the branches of a forest, after various turnings, we both at length got home in safety. Adieu.

P. L., March 21, 1760.

# LETTER IX

## The Chinese Philosopher's Son
## Made A Slave In Persia

From the same.

The letter, which came by the way of Smyrna, and which you sent me unopened, was from my son. As I have permitted you to take copies of all those I sent to China, you might have made no ceremony in opening those directed to me. Either in joy or sorrow, my friend should participate in my feelings. It would give pleasure, to see a good man pleased at my success; it would give almost equal pleasure, to see him sympathise at my disappointment.

Every account I receive from the East seems to come loaded with some new affliction. My wife and daughter were taken from me, and yet I sustained the loss with intrepidity; my son is made a slave among the barbarians, which was the only blow, that could have reached my heart: yes, I will indulge the transports of nature for a little, in order to show I can overcome them in the end. True magnanimity consists, not in never falling, but in rising every time we fall.

When our mighty emperor had published his displeasure at my departure, and seized upon all that was mine, my son was privately secreted from his resentment. Under the protection and guardianship of Fum Hoam, the best and the wisest of all the inhabitants of China, he was for some time instructed in the learning of the missionaries, and the wisdom of the East. But, hearing of my adventures, and incited by filial piety, he was resolved to follow my fortunes, and share my distress.

He passed the confines of China in disguise, hired himself as a camel-driver to a caravan that was crossing the deserts of Thibet, and was within one day's journey of the river Laur, which divides that country from India, when a body of wandering Tartars, falling unexpectedly upon the caravan, plundered it, and made those who escaped their first fury slaves. By those he was led into the extensive and desolate regions, that border on the shores of the Aral lake.

Here he lived by hunting; and was obliged to supply every day a certain proportion of the spoil, to regale his savage masters. His learning, his virtues, and even his beauty, were qualifications that no way served to recommend him; they knew no merit, but that of providing large quantities of milk and raw flesh; and were sensible of no happiness, but that of rioting on the undressed meal.

Some merchants from Mesched, however, coming to trade with the Tartars for slaves, he was sold among the number, and led into the kingdom of Persia, where he is now detained. He is there obliged to watch the looks of a voluptuous and cruel master, a man fond of pleasure, yet incapable of refinement, whom many years' service in war has taught pride, but not bravery.

That treasure which I still keep within my bosom, my child, my all that was left to me, is now a slave. Good heavens! Why was this? Why have I been introduced into this mortal apartment, to be a spectator of my own misfortunes, and the misfortunes of my fellow-creatures? Wherever I turn, what a labyrinth of doubt, error, and disappointment appears! Why was I brought into being; or what purposes made; from whence have I come; whither strayed; or to what regions am I hastening? Reason cannot resolve. It lends a ray to show the horrors of my prison, but not a light to guide me to escape them. Ye boasted revelations of the earth, how little do you aid the enquiry!

How am I surprised at the inconsistency of the Magi! Their two principles of good and evil affright me. The Indian who bathes his visage in urine, and calls it piety, strikes me with astonishment. The Christian, who believes in three Gods, is highly absurd. The Jews, who pretend that Deity is pleased with the effusion of blood, are not less displeasing. I am equally surprised, that rational beings can come from the extremities of the earth, in order to kiss a stone, or scatter pebbles. How contrary to reason are those; and yet all pretend to teach me to be happy!

Surely all men are blind and ignorant of truth. Mankind wanders, unknowing his way, from morning till evening. Where shall we turn after happiness; or is it wisest to desist from the pursuit? Like reptiles in a corner of some stupendous palace, we peep from our holes, look about us, wonder at all we see, but are ignorant of the great architect's design. Oh for a revelation so of Himself, for a plan of His universal system! Oh for the reasons of our creation; or why were we created to be thus unhappy! If we are to experience no other felicity but what this life affords, then are we miserable indeed; if we are born only to look about us, repine and die, then has Heaven been guilty of injustice. If this life terminates my existence, I despise the blessings of Providence, and the wisdom of the giver; if this life be my all, let the following epitaph be written on the tomb of Altangi:

'By My Father's Crimes I Received This; By My Own Crimes I Bequeath It To My Posterity!'

P.L., March 24, 1760.

# LETTER X

## The Character Of The Man In Black, With Some Instances Of His Inconsistent Conduct

To the same.

Though fond of many acquaintances, I desire an intimacy only with a few. The Man in Black, whom I have often mentioned, is one whose friendship I could wish to acquire, because he possesses my esteem. His manners, it is true, are tinctured with some strange inconsistencies; and he may be justly termed an humorist in a nation of humorists. Though he is generous even to profusion, he affects to be thought a prodigy of parsimony and prudence; though his conversation be replete with the most sordid and selfish maxims, his heart is dilated with the most unbounded love. I have known him profess himself a man-hater, while his cheek was glowing with compassion; and, while his looks were softened into pity, I have heard him use the language of the most unbounded ill nature. Some affect humanity and tenderness; others boast of having such dispositions from nature: but he is the only man I ever knew, who seemed ashamed of his natural benevolence. He takes as much pains to hide his feelings, as any hypocrite would, to conceal his indifference; but, on every unguarded moment, the mask drops off, and reveals him to the most superficial observer.

In one of our late excursions into the country, happening to discourse upon the provision that was made for the poor in England, he seemed amazed how any of his countrymen could be so foolishly weak as to relieve occasional objects of charity, when the laws had made such ample provision for their support.

'In every parish-house', says he, 'the poor are supplied with food, clothes, fire, and a bed to lie on; they want no more; I desire no more myself; yet still they seem discontented. I am surprised at the inactivity of our magistrates, in not taking up such vagrants, who are only a weight upon the industrious; I am surprised that the people are found to relieve them, when they must be at the same time sensible that it in some measure encourages idleness, extravagance, and imposture. Were I to advise any man for whom I had the least regard, I would caution him by all means not to be imposed upon by their false pretences; let me assure you, sir, they are impostors, every one of them, and rather merit a prison than relief.'

He was proceeding in this strain, earnestly to dissuade me from an imprudence of which I am seldom guilty, when an old man, who still had about him the remnants of tattered finery, implored our compassion. He assured us: compassion; that he was no common beggar, but forced into the shameful profession, to support a dying wife and five hungry children. Being prepossessed against such falsehoods, his story had not the least influence upon me; but it was quite otherwise with the Man in Black: I could see it visibly operate upon his countenance, and effectually interrupt his harangue. I could easily perceive that his heart burned to relieve the five starving children; but he seemed ashamed to discover his weakness to me. While he thus hesitated between compassion and pride, I pretended to look another way; and he seized this opportunity of giving the poor petitioner a piece of silver, bidding him at the same time, in order that I should hear, go work for his bread, and not tease passengers with such impertinent falsehoods for the future.

As he had fancied himself quite unperceived, he continued, as we proceeded, to rail against beggars with as much animosity as before: he threw in some episodes on his own amazing prudence and economy, with his profound skill in discovering impostors; he explained the manner in which he would deal with beggars, were he a magistrate; hinted at enlarging some of the prisons for their reception; and told two stories of ladies, that were robbed by beggar-men. He was beginning a third to the same purpose, when a sailor with a wooden leg once more crossed our walks, desiring our pity, and blessing our limbs. I was for going on without taking any notice, but my friend, looking wistfully upon the poor petitioner, bid me stop, and he would show me with how much ease he could at any time detect an impostor.

He now, therefore, assumed a look of importance, and in an angry tone began to examine the sailor, demanding in what engagement he was thus disabled and rendered unfit for service. The sailor replied, in a tone as angrily as he, that he had been an officer on board a private ship of war, and that he had lost his leg abroad, in defence of those who did nothing at home. At this reply, all my friend's importance vanished in a moment; he had not a single question more to ask: he now only studied what method he should take to relieve him unobserved. He had, however, no easy part to act, as he was obliged to preserve the appearance of ill-nature before me, and yet relieve himself by relieving the sailor. Casting, therefore, so furious a look upon some bundles of chips, which the fellow carried in a string at his back, my friend demanded how he sold his matches; but, not waiting for a reply, desired, in a surly tone, to have a shilling's worth. The sailor seemed at first surprised at his demand, but soon recollecting himself, and presenting his whole bundle, 'Here, master,' says he, 'take all my cargo, and a blessing into the bargain'.

It is impossible to describe with what an air of triumph my friend marched off with his new purchase; he assured me that he was firmly of opinion that those fellows must have stolen their goods, who could thus afford to sell them for half value. He informed me of several different uses to which those chips might be applied; he expatiated largely upon the savings that would result from lighting, candles with a match, instead of thrusting them into the fire. He averred, that he would as soon have parted with a tooth as his money to those vagabonds, unless for some valuable consideration.

I cannot tell how long this panegyric upon frugality and matches might have continued, had not his attention been called off by another object more distressful than either of the former. A woman in rags, with one child in her arms, and another on her back, was attempting to sing ballads, but with such a mournful voice, that it was difficult to determine whether she was singing or crying. A wretch, who in the deepest distress still aimed at good-humour, was an object my friend was by no means capable of withstanding: his vivacity and his discourse were instantly interrupted; upon this occasion, his very dissimulation had forsaken him. Even in my presence, he immediately applied his hands to his pockets, in order to relieve her; but guess his confusion, when he found he had already given away all the money, he carried about him, to former objects. The misery painted in the woman's visage was not half so strongly expressed, as the agony in his. He continued to search for some time, but to no purpose, till, at length recollecting himself, with a face of ineffable good-nature, as he had no money, he put into her hands his shilling's worth of matches.

P. L., April 3, 1760.

# LETTER XI

## The History Of The Man In Black

To the same.

As there appeared something reluctantly good in the character of my companion, I must own it surprised me what could be his motives for thus concealing virtues, which others take such pains to display. I was unable to repress my desire of knowing the history of a man, who thus seemed to act under continual restraint, and whose benevolence was rather the effect of appetite than reason.

It was not, however, till after repeated solicitations he thought proper to gratify my curiosity. 'If you are fond', says he, 'of hearing hairbreadth 'scapes, my history must certainly please; for I have been for twenty years upon the very verge of starving, without ever being starved.

'My father, the younger son of a good family, was possessed of a small living in the church. His education was above his fortune, and his generosity greater than his education. Poor as he was, he had his flatterers, still poorer than himself; for every dinner he gave them, they returned an equivalent in praise; and this was all he wanted. The same ambition, that actuates a monarch at the head of an army, influenced my father at the head of his table: he told the story of the ivy-tree, and that was laughed at; he repeated the jest of the two scholars and one pair of breeches, and the company laughed at that; but the story of Taffy in the sedan-chair was sure to set the table in a roar: thus his pleasure increased in proportion to the pleasure he gave; he loved all the world, and he fancied all the world loved him.

'As his fortune was but small, he lived up to the very extent of it; he had no intentions of leaving his children money, for that was dross; he was resolved they should have learning; for learning, he used to observe, was better than silver or gold. For this purpose, he undertook to instruct us himself; and took as much pains to form our morals, as to improve our understanding. We were told that universal benevolence was what first cemented society: we were taught to consider all the wants of mankind as our own; to regard 'the human face divine' with affection and esteem; he wound us up to mere machines of pity, and rendered us incapable of withstanding the slightest impulse, made either by real or fictitious distress:' in a word, we were perfectly instructed in the art of giving away thousands, before we were taught the more necessary qualifications of getting a farthing.

'I cannot avoid imagining, that, thus refined by his lessons out of all my suspicion, and divested of even all the little cunning which nature had given me, I resembled, upon my first entrance into the busy and insidious world, one of those gladiators, who were exposed without armour in the amphitheatre at Rome. My father, however, who had only seen the world on one side, seemed to triumph in my superior discernment; though my whole stock of wisdom consisted in being able to talk like himself upon subjects, that once were useful, because they were then topics of the busy world, but that now were utterly useless, because connected with the busy world no longer.

'The first opportunity he had of finding his expectations disappointed was in the very middling figure I made in the

university: he had flattered himself that he should soon see
me rising into the foremost rank in literary recitation, but was
mortified to find me utterly unnoticed and unknown. His disappointment might have been partly ascribed to his having
overrated my talents and partly to my dislike of mathematical
reasonings, at a time when my imagination and memory, yet
unsatisfied, were more eager after new objects, than desirous of
reasoning upon those I knew. This did not, however, please my
tutors, who observed, indeed, that I was a little dull; but at the
same time allowed, that I seemed to be very good-natured, and
had no harm in me.

'After I had resided at college seven years, my father died, and
left me—his blessing. Thus shoved from shore without ill-nature
to protect, or cunning to guide, or proper stores to subsist me
in so dangerous a voyage, I was obliged to embark in the wide
world at twenty-two. But, in order to settle in life, my friends
advised (for they always advise when they begin to despise us),
they advised me, I say, to go into orders.

'To be obliged to wear a long wig, when I liked a short one,
or a black coat, when I generally dressed in brown, I thought was
such a restraint upon my liberty, that I absolutely rejected the
proposal. A priest in England is not the same mortified creature
with a bonze in China: with us, not he that fasts best, but eats
best, is reckoned the best liver; yet I rejected a life of luxury,
indolence, and ease, from no other consideration but that boyish
one of dress. So that my friends were now perfectly satisfied I
was undone; and yet they thought it a pity for one, who had not
the least harm in him and was so very good-natured.

'Poverty naturally begets dependence, and I was admitted
as flatterer to a great man. At first, I was surprised that the
situation of a flatterer at a great man's table could be thought
disagreeable; there was no great trouble in listening attentively,
when his lordship spoke, and laughing, when he looked round
for applause. This even good manners might have obliged me
to perform. I found, however, too soon, that his lordship was

a greater dunce than myself; and from that very moment my power of flattery was at an end. I now rather aimed at setting him right, than at receiving his absurdities with submission: to flatter those we do not know is an easy task; but to flatter our intimate acquaintances, all whose foibles are strongly in our eye, is drudgery insupportable. Every time I now opened my lips in praise, my falsehood went to my conscience; his lordship soon perceived me to be unfit for service; I was therefore discharged; my patron at the same time being graciously pleased to observe, that he believed I was tolerably good-natured, and had not the least harm in me.

'Disappointed in ambition, I had recourse to love. A young lady, who lived with her aunt, and was possessed of a pretty fortune in her own disposal, had given me, as I fancied, some reason to expect success. The symptoms by which I was guided were striking. She had always laughed with me at her awkward acquaintance, and at her aunt among the number; she always observed, that a man of sense would make a better husband than a fool, and I was constantly applied the observation in my own favour. She continually talked, in my company, of friendship and the beauties of the mind, and spoke of Mr. Shrimp my rival's high-heeled shoes with detestation. These were circumstances, which I thought strongly in my favour; so, after resolving and resolving, I had courage enough to tell her my mind. Miss heard my proposal with serenity, seeming at the same time to study the figures of her fan. Out at last it came. There was but one small objection to complete our happiness, which was no more than—that she was married three months before to Mr. Shrimp, with high-heeled shoes! By way of consolation, however, she observed, that, though I was disappointed in her, my address to her aunt would probably kindle her into sensibility; as the old lady always allowed me to be very good-natured, and not to have the least share of harm in me.

'Yet still I had friends, numerous friends, and to them I was resolved to apply. O friendship, thou fond soother of the human breast, to thee we fly in every calamity; to thee the wretched seek for succour; on thee the care-tired son of misery fondly relies: from thy kind assistance the unfortunate always hopes relief, and may be ever sure of disappointment. My first application was to a city scrivener, who had frequently offered to lend me money, when he knew I did not want it. I informed him, that now was the time to put his friendship to the test; that I wanted to borrow a couple of hundreds for a certain occasion, and was resolved to take it up from him. 'And pray, sir,' cried my friend, 'do you want all this money?'

'Indeed, I never wanted it more,' returned I.

'I am sorry for that,' cries the scrivener, 'with all my heart; for they who want money when they come to borrow, will always want money when they should come to pay.'

'From him I flew, with indignation, to one of the best friends I had in the world, and made the same request.

'Indeed, Mr. Drybone,' cries my friend, 'I always thought it would come to this. You know, sir, I would not advise you but for your own good; but your conduct has hitherto been ridiculous in the highest degree, and some of your acquaintance always thought you a very silly fellow. Let me see—you want two hundred pounds. Do you only want two hundred, sir, exactly?'

'To confess a truth,' returned I, 'I shall want three hundred; but then, I have another friend, from whom I can borrow the rest.'

'Why, then,' replied my friend, ' if you would take my advice (and you know I should not presume to advise you but for your own good), I would recommend it to you to borrow the whole sum from that other friend; and then one note will serve for all, you know.'

'Poverty now began to come fast upon me; yet instead of growing more provident or cautious as I grew poor, I became every day more indolent and simple. A friend was arrested for fifty pounds; I was unable to extricate him, except by becoming his bail. When at liberty, he fled from his creditors, and left me to take his place. In prison I expected greater satisfactions, than I had enjoyed at large. I hoped to converse with men in this new world, simple and believing like myself; but I found them as cunning and as cautious, as those in the world I had left behind. They spunged up my money, while it lasted, borrowed my coals, and never paid for them, and cheated me, when I played at cribbage. All this was done, because they believed me to be very good-natured, and knew that I had no harm in me.

'Upon my first entrance into this mansion, which is to some the abode of despair, I felt no sensations different from those I experienced abroad. I was now on one side of the door, and those who were unconfined were on the other: this was all the difference between us. At first, indeed, I felt some uneasiness, in considering how I should be able to provide this week for the wants of the week ensuing; but, after some time, if I found myself sure of eating one day, I never troubled my head how I was to be supplied another. I seized every precarious meal with the utmost good-humour; indulged no rants of spleen at my situation; never called down Heaven and all the stars to behold me dining upon a halfpenny-worth of radishes; my very companions were taught to believe that I liked salad better than mutton. I contented myself with thinking, that all my life I should either eat white bread or brown; considered that all that happened was best; laughed, when I was not in pain, took the world as it went, and read Tacitus often, for want of more books and company.

'How long I might have continued in this torpid state of simplicity I cannot tell, had I not been roused by seeing an old acquaintance, whom I knew to be a prudent blockhead, preferred to a place in the government. I now found that I had pursued a wrong track, and that the true way of being able to relieve others was first to aim at independence myself: my immediate care, therefore, was to leave my present habitation, and make an entire reformation in my conduct and behaviour.

For a free, open, undesigning deportment, I put on that of close-
ness, prudence, and economy. One of the most heroic actions
I ever performed, and for which I shall praise myself as long as
I live, was the refusing half-a-crown to an old acquaintance, at
the time when he wanted it, and I had it to spare; for this alone
I deserve to be decreed an ovation.

'I now, therefore, pursued a course of uninterrupted frugality, seldom wanted a dinner, and was, consequently, invited to
twenty. I soon began to get the character of a saving hunks that
had money, and insensibly grew into esteem. Neighbours have
asked my advice in the disposal of their daughters; and I have
always taken care not to give any. I have contracted a friendship with an alderman, only by observing, that, if we take a
farthing from a thousand pounds, it will be a thousand pounds
no I longer. I have been invited to a pawnbroker's table, by so
pretending to hate gravy; and am now actually upon treaty of
marriage with a rich widow, for only having observed that the
bread was rising. If ever I am asked a question, whether I know
it or not, instead of answering, I only smile and look wise. If a
charity is proposed, I go about with the hat, but put nothing
in myself. If a wretch solicits my pity, I observe that the world
is filled with impostors, and take a certain method of not being
deceived by never relieving. In short, I now find the truest way
of finding esteem, even from the indigent, is to give away nothing, and thus have much in our power to give.'

P. L., April 9, 1760.

# LETTER XII

## The Philosopher's Son Describes
## A Lady, His Fellow Captive

From Ffingpo, a Slave in Persia to Altangi, a travelling Philosopher of China, by the way of Moscow.

Fortune has made me the slave of another, but nature and inclination render me entirely subservient to you; a tyrant commands my body, but you are master of my heart. And yet let not thy inflexible nature condemn me when I confess, that I find my soul shrink with my circumstances. I feel my mind, not less than my body, bend beneath the rigours of servitude; the master whom I serve grows every day more formidable. In spite of reason, which should teach me to despise him, his hideous image fills even my dreams with horror.

A few days ago, a Christian slave, who wrought in the gardens, happening to enter an arbour, where the tyrant was entertaining the ladies of his harem with coffee, the unhappy captive was instantly stabbed to the heart for is intrusion. I have been preferred to his place, which, though less laborious than my former station, is yet more ungrateful, as it brings me nearer him, whose presence excites sensations at once of disgust and apprehension.

Into what a state of misery are the modern Persians fallen! A nation, famous for setting the world an example of freedom, is now become a land of tyrants, and a den of slaves. The house-less Tartar of Kamschatka, who enjoys his herbs and his fish in unmolested freedom, may be envied, if compared to the thousands, who pine here in hopeless servitude, and curse the day that gave them being. Is this just dealing, Heaven, to render millions wretched, to swell up the happiness of a few? Cannot the powerful of this earth be happy, without our sighs and tears? Must every luxury of the great be woven from the calamities of the poor? It must, it must surely, be that this jarring discordant life is but the prelude to some future harmony: the soul, attuned to virtue here, shall go from hence to fill up the universal choir, where Tien presides in person; where there shall be no tyrants to frown, no shackles to bind, nor no whips to threaten; where I shall once more meet my father with rapture, and give a loose to filial piety; where I shall hang on his neck, and hear the wisdom of his lips, and thank him for all the happiness, to which he has introduced me.

The wretch, whom fortune has made my master, has lately purchased several slaves of both sexes; among the rest, I hear a Christian captive talked of with admiration. The eunuch who bought her, and who is accustomed to survey beauty with indif-ference, speaks of her with emotion. Her pride, however, aston-ishes her attendant slaves not less than her beauty. It is reported that she refuses the warmest solicitations of her haughty lord; he has even offered to make her one of his four wives upon changing her religion, and conforming to his. It is so probable she cannot refuse such extraordinary offers, and her delay is perhaps intended to enhance her favours.

I have just now seen her; she inadvertently approached the place, without a veil, where I sat writing. She seemed to regard the heavens alone with fixed attention; there her most ardent gaze was directed. Genius of the sun! What unexpected softness! What animated grace! Her beauty seemed the transparent covering of virtue. Celestial beings could not wear a look of more perfection; while sorrow humanized her form, and mixed my admiration with pity. I rose from the bank on which I sat, and she retired: happy that none observed us; for such in interview might have been fatal.

I have regarded, till now, the opulence and the power of my tyrant without envy. I saw him with a mind incapable of enjoying the gifts of fortune, and, consequently, regarded him as one loaded, rather than enriched, with its favours; but at present, when I think that so much beauty is reserved only for him, that so many charms should be lavished on a wretch incapable of feeling the greatness of the blessing, I own I feel a reluctance to which I have hitherto been a stranger.

But let not my father impute those uneasy sensations to so trifling a cause as love. No; never let it be thought that your son, and the pupil of the wise Fum Hoam, could stoop to so degrading a passion: I am only displeased at seeing so much excellence so unjustly disposed of.

The uneasiness which I feel is not for myself, but for the beautiful Christian. When I reflect on the barbarity of him, for whom she is designed, I pity, indeed I pity her; when I think that she must only share one heart, who deserves to command a thousand, excuse me if I feel an emotion, which universal benevolence extorts from me. As I am convinced that you take a pleasure in those sallies, of humanity, and are particularly pleased with compassion, I could not avoid discovering the sensibility with which I felt this beautiful stranger's distress. I have for a while forgot, in hers, the miseries of my own hopeless situation: the tyrant grows every day more severe; and love, which softens all other minds into tenderness, seems only to have increased his severity. Adieu.

P. L., May 12, 1760.

# LETTER XIII

## A Continuation Of His Correspondence - The Beautiful Captive Consents To Marry Her Lord

From the same.

The whole harem is filled with a tumultuous joy; Zelis, the beautiful captive, has consented to embrace the religion of Mahomet, and become one of the wives of the fastidious Persian. It is impossible to describe the transport that sits on every face on this occasion. Music and feasting fill every apartment; the most miserable slave seems to forget his chains, and sympathises with the happiness of Mostadad. The herb we tread beneath our feet is not made more for our use, than every slave around him for their imperious master; mere machines of obedience, they wait with silent assiduity, feel his pains, and rejoice in his exultation. Heavens, how much is requisite to make one man happy!

Twelve of the most beautiful slaves, and I among the number, have got orders to prepare for carrying him in triumph to the bridal apartment. The blaze of perfumed torches are to imitate the day; the dancers and singers are hired at a' vast expense. The nuptials are to be celebrated on the approaching feast of

Barboura, when an hundred taels in gold are to be distributed among the barren wives, in order to pray for fertility from the approaching union.

What will not riches procure? An hundred domestics, who curse the tyrant in their souls, are commanded to wear a face of joy; and they are joyful. An hundred flatterers are ordered to attend, and they fill his ears with praise. Beauty, all-command-ing beauty, 'sues for admittance, and scarcely receives an answer: even love itself seems to wait upon fortune; or, though the pas-sion be only feigned, yet it wears every appearance of sincerity; and what greater pleasure can even true sincerity confer, or what would the rich have more?

Mostadad, O my father, is no philosopher; and yet he seems perfectly contented with ignorance. Possessed of numberless slaves, camels, and women, he desires no greater possession. He never opened the page of Mencius, and yet all the slaves tell me that he is happy. Forgive the weakness of my nature, if I sometimes feel my heart rebellious to the dictates of wisdom, and eager for happiness like his. Yet why wish for his wealth, when his ignorance: to be, like him, incapable of sentimental pleasures, incapable of feeling the happiness of making others happy, incapable of teaching the beautiful Zelis philosophy?

What, shall I in a transport of passion give up the golden mean, the universal harmony, the unchanging essence, for the possession of an hundred camels, as many slaves, thirty-five beautiful horses, and seventy-three fine women! First blast me to the centre; degrade me beneath the most degraded; pare my nails, ye powers of Heaven, ere I would stoop to such an exchange! What, part with philosophy, which teaches me to suppress my passions, instead of gratifying them, which teaches me even to divest my soul of passion, which teaches serenity in the midst of tortures; philosophy, by which even now I am so very serene, and so very much at ease, to be persuaded to part with it for any other enjoyment! Never, never, even though persuasion spoke in the accents of Zelis!

A female slave informs me that the bride is to be arrayed in a tissue of silver, and her hair adorned with the largest pearls of Ormus. But why tease you with particulars, in which we both are so little concerned? The pain I feel in separation throws a gloom over, my mind, which, in this scene of universal joy, I fear may be attributed to some other cause. How wretched are those who are, like me, denied even the last resource of misery, their tears! Adieu.

P. L., May 14, 1760.

# LETTER XIV

## The Behaviour Of The Congregation In St Paul's Church At Prayers

From Lien Chi Altangi to Fum Hoam.

Some time since I sent thee, O holy disciple of Confucius, an account of the grand abbey, or mausoleum, of the kings and heroes of this nation; I have since been introduced to a temple, not so ancient, but far superior in beauty and magnificence. In this, which is the most considerable of the empire, there are no pompous inscriptions, no flattery paid the dead, but all is elegant and awfully simple. There are, however, a few rags hung round the walls, which have, at a vast expense, been taken from the enemy in the present war. The silk, of which they are composed, when new, might be valued at half a string of copper money in China; yet this wise people fitted out a fleet and an army, in order to seize them; though now grown old, and scarcely capable of being patched up into a handkerchief. By this conquest, the English are said to have gained, and the French to have lost, much honour. Is the honour of European nations placed only in tattered silk?

In this temple I was permitted to remain during the whole service; and were you not already acquainted with the religion of the English, you might, from my description, be inclined to believe them as grossly idolatrous, as the disciples of Lao. The idol, which they seem to address, strides like a colossus over the door of the inner temple, which here, as with the Jews, is esteemed the most sacred part of the building. Its oracles are delivered in an hundred various tones, which seem to inspire the worshippers with enthusiasm and awe: an old woman, who appeared to be the priestess, was employed in various attitudes, as she felt the inspiration. When it began to speak, all the people remained fixed in silent attention, nodding assent, looking approbation, appearing highly edified by those sounds, which, to a stranger, might seem inarticulate and unmeaning.

When the idol had done speaking, and the priestess had locked up its lungs with a key, observing almost all the company leaving the temple, I concluded the service was over, and, taking my hat, was going to walk away with the crowd, when I was stopped by the Man in Black, who assured me that the ceremony had scarcely yet begun. 'What!' cried I, 'do I not see almost the whole body of the worshippers leaving the church? Would you persuade me that such numbers who profess religion and morality would, in this shameless manner, quit the temple, before the service was concluded? You surely mistake; not even the Kalmucks would be guilty of such an indecency, though all the object of their worship was but a joint-stool.'

My friend seemed to blush for his countrymen, assuring me that those, whom I saw running away, were only a parcel of musical blockheads, whose passion was merely for sounds, and whose heads were as empty as a fiddle-case: those who remain behind, says he, are the true religious; they make use of music to warm their hearts, and to lift them to a proper pitch of rapture; examine their behaviour, and you will confess there are some among us, who practise true devotion.

I now looked round me as directed, but saw nothing of that fervent devotion, which he had promised: one of the worshippers appeared to be ogling the company through a glass; another was fervent, not in addresses to Heaven, but to his mistress; a third whispered; a fourth took snuff; and the priest himself, in a drowsy tone, read over the duties of the day.

'Bless my eyes!' cried I, as I happened to look towards the door, 'What do I see? One of the worshippers fallen fast asleep, and actually sunk down on his cushion! He is now enjoying the benefit of a trance; or does he receive the influence of some mysterious vision?'

'Alas! alas!' replied my companion, 'no such thing; he has only had the misfortune of eating too hearty a dinner, and finds it impossible to keep his eyes open.'

Turning to another part of the temple, I perceived a young lady just in the same circumstances and attitude: 'Strange', I cried; 'can she, too, have over-eaten herself?'

'Oh, fie!' replied my friend, 'you now grow censorious. She grew drowsy from eating too much! That would be profanation. She only sleeps now, from having sat up all night at a brag party.'

'Turn me where I will, then,' says I, 'I can perceive no single symptom of devotion among the worshippers, except from that old woman in the corner, who sits so groaning behind the long sticks of a mourning fan; she indeed seems greatly edified with what she hears.'

'Aye,' replied my friend, 'I knew we should find some to catch you: I know her; that is the deaf lady, who lives in the cloisters.'

In short, the remissness of behaviour in almost all the worshippers, and some even of the guardians, struck me with surprise. I had been taught to believe, that none were ever promoted to offices in the temple, but men remarkable for their superior sanctity, learning, and rectitude; that there was no such thing heard of as persons being introduced into the church, merely to oblige a senator, or provide for the younger branch of a noble family: I expected, as their minds were continually set upon ) heavenly things, to see their eyes directed there also; and hoped,

from their behaviour, to perceive their inclinations corresponding with their duty. But I am since informed, that some are
appointed to preside over temples they never visit; and, while
they receive all the money, are contented with letting others
do all the good. Adieu.

P. L.., May, 28, 1760.

# LETTER XV

## The Character Of An Important Trifler

From the same.

Though naturally pensive, yet I am fond of gay company, and take every opportunity of thus dismissing the mind from duty. From this motive, I am often found in the centre of a crowd; and, wherever pleasure is to be sold, am always a purchaser. In those places, without being remarked by any, I join in whatever goes forward; work my passions into a similitude of frivolous earnestness, shout as they shout, and condemn as they happen to disapprove. A mind thus sunk for a while below its natural standard is qualified for stronger flights, as those first retire, who would spring forward with greater vigour.

Attracted by the serenity of the evening, my friend and I lately went to gaze upon the company in one of the public walks near the city. Here we sauntered together for some time, either praising the beauty of such as were handsome, or the dresses of such as had nothing else to recommend them. We had gone thus deliberately forward for some time, when, stopping on a sudden, my friend caught me by the elbow, and led me out of the public walk. I could perceive by the quickness of his pace, and by his frequently looking behind, that he was attempting to avoid somebody who followed: we now turned to the right, then to the left; as we went forward, he still went faster; but in vain: the person, whom he attempted to escape, hunted us through every doubling, and gained upon us each moment, so that at last we fairly stood still, resolving to face what we could not avoid.

Our pursuer soon came up, and joined us with all the familiarity of an old acquaintance.

'My dear Drybone,' cries he, shaking my friend's hand, 'where have you been hiding this half a century? Positively I had fancied you were gone to cultivate matrimony, and your estate in the country.'

During the reply, I had an opportunity of surveying the appearance of our new companion: his hat was pinched up with peculiar smartness; his looks were pale, thin, and sharp; round his neck he wore a broad, black riband, and in his bosom a buckle studded with glass; his coat was trimmed with tarnished twist; he wore by his side a sword with a black hilt; and his stockings of silk, though newly washed, were grown yellow by long service. I was so much engaged with the peculiarity of his dress, that I so attended only to the latter part of my friend's reply, in which he complimented Mr. Tibbs on the taste of his clothes, and the bloom in his countenance.

'Pshaw, pshaw, Will,' cried the figure, 'no more of that, if you love me: you know I hate flattery, on my soul I do; and yet, to be sure, an intimacy with the great will improve one's appearance, and a course of venison will fatten; and yet, faith, I despise the great as much as you do; but there are a great many damn'd honest fellows amongst them, and we must not quarrel with one half, because the other wants weeding. If they were all such as my Lord Mudler, one of the most good-natured creatures that ever squeezed a lemon, I should myself be among the number of their admirers. I was yesterday to dine at the Duchess of

Piccadilly's. My lord was there. 'Ned,' says he to me, 'Ned,' says he, 'I'll hold gold to silver I can tell where you were poaching last night.' 'Poaching, my lord?' says I: 'faith, you have missed already; for I staid at home, and let the girls poach for me. That's my way: I take a fine woman as some animals do their prey; stand still, and, swoop, they fall into my mouth.'

'Ah, Tibbs, thou art a happy fellow,' cried my companion, with looks of infinite pity; 'I hope your fortune is as much improved as your understanding in such company?'

'Improved!' replied the other; 'you shall know— but let it go no farther—a great secret—five hundred a year to begin with—my lord's word of honour for it. His lordship took me down in his own chariot yesterday, and we had a tête-à-tête dinner in the country, where we talked of nothing else.'

'I fancy you forget, sir,' cried I; 'you told us but this moment of your dining yesterday in town.'

'Did I say so?' replied he coolly; 'to be sure, if I said so, it was so. Dined in town! Egad, now I do remember, I did dine in town; but I dined in the country too; for you must know, my boys, I eat two dinners. By the by, I am grown as nice as the devil in my eating. I'll tell you a pleasant affair about that: we were a select party of us to dine at Lady Grogram's, an affected piece, but let it go no farther—a secret. Well, there happened to be no asafoetida in the sauce to a turkey, upon which, says I, I'll hold a thousand guineas, and say done first, that—But, dear Drybone, you are an honest creature; lend me half-a-crown for a minute or two, or so, just till——; but hearken, ask me for it the next time we meet, or it may be twenty to one but I forget to pay you.'

When he left us, our conversation naturally turned upon so extraordinary a character.

'His very dress', cries my friend, 'is not less extraordinary than his conduct If you meet him this days you find him in rags; if the next, in embroidery. With those persons of distinction, of whom he talks so familiarly, he has scarce a coffeehouse acquaintance.

However, both for the interests of society; and perhaps for his own, Heaven has made him poor; and while all the world perceive his wants, he fancies them concealed from every eye. An agreeable companion, because he understands flattery; and all must be pleased with the first part of his conversation, though all are sure of its ending with a demand on their purse. While his youth countenances the levity of his conduct, he may thus earn a precarious subsistence; but, when age comes on, the gravity of which is incompatible with buffoonery, then will he find himself forsaken by all; condemned in the decline of life to hang upon some rich family whom he once despised, there to undergo all the ingenuity of studied contempt, to be employed only as a spy upon the servants, or a bugbear to fright the children into obedience.' Adieu.

P. L., July 2, 1760.

# LETTER XVI

## His Character Continued, With That Of His Wife, His House, And Furniture

To the same.

'I am apt to fancy I have contracted a new acquaintance, whom it will be no easy matter to shake off. My little beau yesterday overtook me again in one of the public walks, and, slapping me on the shoulder, saluted me with an air of the most perfect familiarity. His dress was the same as usual, except that he had more powder in his hair, wore a dirtier shirt, a pair of temple spectacles, and his hat under his arm.

As I knew him to be an harmless, amusing little thing, I could not return his smiles with any degree of severity; so we walked forward on terms of the utmost intimacy, and in a few minutes discussed all the usual topics preliminary to particular conversation. The oddities that marked his character, however, soon began to appear; he bowed to several well-dressed persons, who, by their manner of returning the compliment, appeared perfect strangers. At intervals he drew out a pocket-book, seeming to take memorandums, before all the company, with much importance and assiduity. In this manner he led through the length of the whole walk, fretting at his absurdities, and fancying myself laughed at, not less than him, by every spectator.

When we were got to the end of our procession, 'Blast me,' cries he, with an air of vivacity, 'I never saw the Park so thin in my life before! There's no company at all to-day; not a single face to be seen.'

'No company!' interrupted I peevishly; 'no company, where there is such a crowd ? Why, man, there's too much. What are the thousands that have been laughing at us but company?'

'Lord, my dear,' returned he, with the utmost good humour, 'you seem immensely chagrined; but, blast me, when the world laughs at me, I laugh at the world, and so we are even. My Lord Trip. Bill Squash the Creolian, and I sometimes make a party at being ridiculous; and so we say and do a thousand things for the joke's sake. But I see you are grave, and, if you are for a fine grave sentimental companion, you shall dine with me and my wife to-day; I must insist on't. I'll introduce you to Mrs. Tibbs, a lady of as elegant qualifications as any in nature; she was bred, but that's between ourselves, under the inspection of the Countess of All-night. A charming body of voice; but no more of that—she shall give us a song. You shall see my little girl too, Carolina Wilhelmina Amelia Tibbs, a sweet pretty creature! I design her for my Lord Drumstick's eldest son; but that's in friendship, let it go no farther: she's but six years old, and yet she walks a minuet, and plays on the guitar immensely already. I intend she shall be as perfect as possible in every accomplishment. In the first place, I'll make her a scholar: I'll teach her Greek myself, and learn that language purposely to instruct her; but let that be a secret.'

Thus saying, without waiting for a reply, he took me by the arm, and hauled me along. We passed through many dark alleys and winding ways; for, from some motives to me unknown, he seemed to have a particular aversion to every frequented street: at last, however, we got to the door of a dismal-looking house in the outlets of the town, where he informed me he chose to reside for the benefit of the air.

We entered the lower door, which ever seemed to lie most hospitably open; and I began to ascend an old and creaking stair-case, when, as he mounted to show me the way, he demanded whether I delighted in prospects; to which answering in the affirmative, 'Then,' says he, 'I shall show you one of the most charming in the world out of my window; we shall see the ships sailing, and the whole country for twenty miles round, tip top, quite high. My Lord Swamp would give ten thousand guineas for such a one; but, as I sometimes pleasantly tell him, I always love to keep my prospects at home, that my friends may come to see me the oftener.'

By this time we were arrived as high as the stairs would permit us to ascend, till we came to what he was facetiously pleased to call the first floor down the chimney; and, knocking at the door, a voice from within demanded : 'Who's there?' My conductor answered that it was him. But, this not satisfying the querist, the voice again repeated the demand; to which he answered louder than before; and now the door was opened by an old woman with cautious reluctance.

When we were got in, he welcomed me to his house with great ceremony, and, turning to the old woman, asked where was her lady?

'Good troth,' replied she, in a peculiar dialect, 'she's washing your twa shirts at the next door, because they nave taken an oath against lending out the tub any longer.'

'My two shirts!' cries he in a tone, that faltered with confusion; 'what does the idiot mean?'

'I ken what I mean weel enough,' replied the other; 'she's washing your twa shirts at the next door, because——'

'Fire and fury, no more of thy stupid explanations!' cried he; 'go and inform her we have got company. Were that Scotch hag,' continued he, turning to me, 'to be for ever in my family, she would never learn politeness, nor forget that absurd poisonous accent of hers, or testify the smallest specimen of breeding or high life; and yet it is very surprising too, as I had her from a parliament man, a friend of mine from the Highlands, one of the politest men in the world; but that's a secret.'

We waited some time for Mrs. Tibbs' arrival, during which interval I had a full opportunity of surveying the chamber and, all its furniture: which consisted of four chairs with old wrought bottoms, that he assured me were his wife's embroidery; a square table that had been once japanned; a cradle in one corner, a lumbering cabinet in the other; a broken shepherdess, and a mandarin without a head, were stuck over the chimney; and round the walls several paltry unframed pictures, which, he observed, were all his own drawing.

'What do you think, sir, of that head in the corner, done in the manner of Grisoni? There's the true keeping in it; it is my own face, and, though there happens to be no likeness, a Countess offered me an hundred for its fellow. I refused her, for, hang it, that would be mechanical, you know.'

The wife at last made her appearance, at once a slattern and a coquette; much emaciated, but still carrying the remains of beauty. She made twenty apologies for being seen in such an odious dishabille, but hoped to be excused, as she had staid out all night at the Gardens with the Countess, who was excessively fond of the horns.

'And, indeed, my dear,' added she, turning to her husband, 'his lordship drank your health in a bumper.'

'Poor Jack,' cries he; 'a dear good-natured creature; I know he loves me. But I hope, my dear, you have given orders for dinner; you need make no great preparations neither; there are but three of us; something elegant and little will do—a turbot, an ortolan, a—'

'Or what do you think, my dear,' interrupts the wife, 'of a nice pretty bit of ox-cheek, piping hot, and dressed with a little of my own sauce?'

'The very thing,' replies he; 'it will eat best with some smart bottled beer; but be sure to let us have the sauce his Grace was so fond of. I hate your immense loads of meat; that is country all over; extreme disgusting to those who are in the least acquainted with high life.'

By this time my curiosity began to abate, and my appetite to increase: the company of fools may at first make us smile, but at last never fails of rendering us melancholy; I therefore pretended to recollect a prior engagement, and, after having shown my respect to the house, according to the fashion of the English, by giving the old servant a piece of money at the door, I took my leave; Mrs. Tibbs assuring me that dinner, if I stayed, would be ready at least in less than two hours.

P. L., Aug. I, 1760.

# LETTER XVII

## A Visitation Dinner Described

To the same.

As the Man in Black takes every opportunity of introducing me to such company, as may serve to indulge my speculative temper, or gratify my curiosity, I was by his influence lately invited to a visitation dinner. To understand this term, you must know that it was formerly the custom here for the principal priests to go about the country once a year, and examine upon the spot whether those of subordinate orders did their duty, or were qualified for the task; whether their temples were kept in proper repair, or the laity pleased with their administration.

Though a visitation of this nature was very useful, yet it was found to be exceedingly troublesome, and for many reasons utterly inconvenient; for, as the principal priests were obliged to attend at court, in order to solicit preferment, it was impossible they could at the same time attend in the country, which was quite out of the road to promotion. If we add to this the gout, which has been, time immemorial, a clerical disorder here, together with the bad wine and ill-dressed provisions, that must

infallibly be served up by the way, it was not strange that the custom has been long discontinued. At present, therefore, every head of the church, instead of going about to visit his priests, is satisfied, if his priests come in a body once a year to visit him; by this means the duty of half a year is despatched in a day. When assembled, he asks each in turn how they have behaved,
and are liked; upon which those who have neglected their duty, or are disagreeable to their congregation, no doubt accuse themselves, and tell him all their faults, for which he reprimands them most severely.

The thoughts of being introduced into a company of philosophers and learned men (for as such I conceived them) gave me no small pleasure. I expected our entertainment would resemble those sentimental banquets so finely described by Xenophon and Plato; I was hoping some Socrates would be brought in from the door, in order to harangue upon divine love: but, as for eating and drinking, I had prepared myself to be disappointed in that particular. I was apprised that fasting and temperance were tenets strongly recommended to the professors of Christianity, and I have seen the frugality and mortification of the priests of the East; so that I expected an entertainment, where we should have much reasoning, and little meat.

Upon being introduced, I confess I found no great signs of mortification in the faces or persons of the company. However, I imputed their florid looks to temperance, and their corpulency to a sedentary way of living. I saw several preparations, indeed, for dinner, but none for philosophy. The company seemed to gaze upon the table with silent expectation; but this I easily excused. Men of wisdom, thought I, are ever slow of speech; they deliver nothing unadvisedly. 'Silence', says Confucius, 'is a friend that will never betray.' They are now probably inventing maxims or hard sayings for their mutual instruction, when some one shall think proper to begin.

My curiosity was now wrought up to the highest pitch. I impatiently looked round to see if any were going to interrupt the mighty pause; when at last one of the company declared that there was a sow in his neighbourhood, that farrowed fifteen pigs at a litter. This I thought a very preposterous, beginning; but just as another was going to second the remark, dinner was served, which interrupted the conversation for that time.

The appearance of dinner, which consisted of a variety of dishes, seemed to diffuse new cheerfulness upon every face; so that I now expected the philosophical conversation to begin, as they improved in good humour. The principal priest, however, opened his mouth with only observing, that the venison had not been kept enough, though he had given strict orders for having it killed ten days before.

'I fear,' continued he, 'it will be found to want the true heathy flavour; you will find nothing of the original wildness in it.'

A priest who sat next him having smelt it, and wiped his nose, 'Ah, my good lord,' cries he, 'you are too modest; it is perfectly fine: everybody knows that nobody understands keeping venison with your lordship.'

'Ay, and partridges, too,' interrupted another; 'I never find them right anywhere else.'

His lordship was going to reply, when a third took off the attention of the company, by recommending the pig as inimitable.

'I fancy, my lord,' continues he, 'it has been smothered in its own blood.'

'If it has been smothered in its blood,' cried a facetious member, helping himself, 'we'll now smother it in egg sauce.'

This poignant piece of humour produced a long loud laugh, which the facetious brother observing, and, now that he was in luck, willing to second his blow, assured the company he would tell them a good story about that.

'As good a story,' cries he, bursting into a violent fit of laughter himself, 'as ever you heard in your lives. There was a farmer in my parish, who used to sup upon wild ducks and flummery; so this farmer—'

'Doctor Marrowfat,' cries his lordship, interrupting him, 'give me leave to drink your health.'

'So being fond of wild ducks and flummery,—'

'Doctor,' adds a gentleman who sat next to him, 'let me advise you to a wing of this turkey.'

'So this farmer being fond—'

'Hob and nob, Doctor; which do you choose, white or red?'

'So being fond of wild ducks and flummery—'

'Take care of your band, sir, it may dip in the gravy.'

The Doctor, now looking round, found not a single eye disposed to listen; wherefore, calling for a glass of wine, he gulped down the disappointment and the tale in a bumper.

The conversation now began to be little more than a rhapsody of exclamations; as each had pretty well satisfied his own appetite, he now found sufficient time to press others. 'Excellent! The very thing! Let me recommend the pig! Do but taste the bacon! Never ate a better thing in my life! Exquisite! Delicious!' This edifying discourse continued through three courses, which lasted as many hours, till every one of the company was unable to swallow or utter anything more.

It is very natural for men, who are abridged in one excess, to break into some other. The clergy here, particularly those who are advanced in years, think, if they are abstemious with regard to women and wine, they may indulge their other appetites without censure. Thus some are found to rise in the morning only to a consultation with their cook about dinner, and, when that has been swallowed, make no other use of their faculties, (if they have any) but to ruminate on the succeeding meal.

A debauch of wine is even more pardonable than this, since one glass insensibly leads on to another, and, instead of sating, whets the appetite. The progressive steps to it are cheerful and seducing; the grave are animated, the melancholy relieved; and there is even classic authority to countenance the excess. But in eating, after nature is once satisfied, every additional morsel brings stupidity and distempers with it, and, as one of their own poets expresses it:

'The soul subsides, and wickedly inclines To seem but mortal, e'en in sound divines'.

Let me suppose, after such a meal as this I have been describing, while all the company are sitting in lethargic silence round the table, groaning under a load of soup, so pig, pork, and bacon; let me suppose, I say, some hungry beggar, with looks of want, peeping through one of the windows, and thus addressing the assembly: 'Prithee, pluck those napkins from your chins; after nature is satisfied, all that you eat extraordinary is my property, and I claim it as mine. It was given you in order to relieve me, and not to oppress yourselves. How can they comfort or instruct others, who can scarce feel their own existence, except from the unsavoury returns of an ill-digested meal? But though neither you nor the cushions you sit upon will hear me, yet the world regards the excesses of its teachers with a prying eye, and notes their conduct with double severity.' I know no other answer any one of the company could make to such an expostulation, but this: 'Friend, you talk of our losing a character, and being disliked by the world; well, and supposing all this to be true, what then, who cares for the world? We'll preach for the world; and the world shall pay us for preaching, whether we like each other or not.'

P. L., July 18, 1760.

# LETTER XVIII

## The Chinese Philosopher's Son Escapes With The Beautiful Captive From Slavery

From Hingpo to Lien Chi Altangi, by the way of Moscow.

You will probably be pleased to see my letter dated from Terki, a city which lies beyond the bounds of the Persian empire: here, blessed with security, with all that is dear, I double my raptures by communicating them to you; the mind sympathizing with the freedom of the body, my whole soul is dilated in gratitude, love, and praise.

Yet, were my own happiness all that inspired my present joy, my raptures might justly merit the imputation of self-interest; but, when I think that the beautiful Zelis is also free, forgive my triumph, when I boast of having rescued from captivity the most deserving object upon earth.

You remember the reluctance she testified at being obliged to marry the tyrant she hated. Her compliance at last was only feigned, in order to gain time to try some future means of escape. During the interval between her promise and the intended performance of it she came, undiscovered, one evening, to the place where I generally retired after the fatigues of the day: her appearance was like that of an aerial genius, when it descends to minister comfort to undisturbed distress; the mild lustre of her eye served to banish my timidity; her accents were sweeter than the echo of some distant symphony.

'Unhappy stranger,' said she, in the Persian language, 'you here perceive one more wretched than thyself! All this solemnity of preparation, this elegance of dress, and the number of my attendants, serve but to increase my miseries; if you have courage to rescue an unhappy woman from approaching ruin, and our detested tyrant, you may depend upon my future gratitude.'

I bowed to the ground, and she left me filled with rapture and astonishment. Night brought me no rest, nor could the ensuing morning calm the anxieties of my mind. I projected a thousand methods for her delivery; but each; when strictly examined, appeared impracticable: in this uncertainty the evening again arrived, and I placed myself on my former station, in hopes of a repeated visit. After some short expectation, the bright perfection again appeared; I bowed, as before, to the ground; when, raising me up, she observed that the time was not to be spent in useless ceremony; she observed that the day following was appointed for the celebration of her nuptials, and that something was to be done that very night for our mutual deliverance. I offered with the utmost humility to pursue whatever scheme she should direct; upon which, she proposed that instant to scale the garden wall, adding that she had prevailed upon a female slave, who was now waiting at the appointed place, to assist her with a ladder.

Pursuant to this information, I led her trembling to the place appointed; but, instead of the slave we expected to see, Mostadad himself was there awaiting our arrival: the wretch in whom we had confided, it seems, had betrayed our design to her master, and he now saw the most convincing proofs of her information. He was just going to draw his sabre, when a principle of avarice repressed his fury; and he resolved, after a severe chastisement, to dispose of me to another master: in the meantime he ordered me to be confined in the strictest manner, and the next day to receive a hundred blows on the soles of my feet.

When the morning came, I was led out in order to receive the punishment, which, from the severity with which it is generally inflicted upon slaves, is worse even than death.

A trumpet was to be the signal for the solemnization of the nuptials of Zelis, and for the infliction of my punishment. Each ceremony, to me equally dreadful, was just going to begin, when we were informed that a large body of Circassian Tartars had invaded the town, and were laying all in ruin. Every person now thought only of saving himself; I instantly unloosed the cords with which I was bound, and, seizing a scimitar from one of the slaves, who had not courage to resist me, flew to the women's apartment, where Zelis was confined, dressed so out for the intended nuptials. I bade her follow me without delay, and, going forward, cut my way through the eunuchs, who made but a faint resistance. The whole city was now a scene of conflagration and terror; every person was willing to save himself, unmindful of others. In this confusion, seizing upon two of the fleetest coursers in the stable of Mostadad, we fled northward towards the kingdom of Circassia. As there were several others flying in the same manner, we passed without notice, and in three days arrived at Terki, a city that lies in a valley within the bosom of the frowning mountains of Caucasus. Here, free from every apprehension of danger, we enjoy all those satisfactions, which are consistent with virtue; though I find my heart at intervals give way to unusual passions, yet, such is my admiration for my fair companion, that I lose even tenderness in distant respect. Though her person demands particular regard even among the beauties of Circassia, yet is her mind far more lovely. How very different is a woman, who thus has cultivated her understanding, and been refined into delicacy of sentiment, from the daughters of the East, whose education is only formed to improve the person. Adieu.

P. L., July 21, 1760.

# LETTER XIX

## The History Of A Philosophic Cobbler

From Lien Chi Altangi to Fum Hoam.

Though not very fond of seeing a pageant myself, yet I am generally pleased with being in the crowd which sees it: it is amusing to observe the effect, which such a spectacle has upon the variety of faces; the pleasure it excites in some, the envy in others, and the wishes it raises in all. With this design, I lately went to see the entry of a foreign ambassador, resolved to make one in the mob, to shout as they shouted, to fix with earnestness upon the same frivolous objects, and participate for a while the pleasures and the wishes of the vulgar.

Struggling here for some time, in order to be first to see the cavalcade as it passed, some one of the crowd unluckily happened to tread upon my shoe; and tore it in such a manner, that I was utterly unqualified to march forward with the main body, and obliged to fall back in the rear. Thus rendered incapable of being a spectator of the show myself, I was at least willing to observe the spectators; and limped behind, like one of the invalids, which follow the march of an army.

In this plight, as I was considering the eagerness that appeared on every face, how some bustled to get foremost, and others contented themselves with taking a transient peep when they could; how some praised the four black servants that were stuck behind one of the equipages, and some the ribands that decorated the horses' necks in another, my attention was called off to an object more extraordinary than any I had yet seen. A poor cobbler sat in his stall by the wayside, and continued to work, while the crowd passed by, without testifying the smallest share of curiosity. I own his want of attention excited mine; and, as I stood in need of his assistance, I thought it best to employ a philosophic cobbler on this occasion. Perceiving my business, therefore, he desired me to enter and sit down, took my shoe in his lap, and began to mend it with his usual indifference and taciturnity.

'How, my friend,' said I to him, 'can you continue to work, while all those fine things are passing by your door?'

'Very fine they are, master,' returned the cobbler, 'for those that like them, to be sure; but what are all so those fine things to me? You don't know what it is to be a cobbler, and so much the better for yourself. Your bread is baked: you may go and see sights the whole day, and eat a warm supper, when you come home at night; but for me, if I should run hunting after all these fine folk, what should I get for ray journey but an appetite, and, God help me, I have too much of that at home already, without stirring out for it. Your people, who may eat four meals a day and a supper at night, are but a bad example to such a one as I. No, master, as God has called me into this world in order to mend old shoes, I have no business with fine folk, and they no business with me.'

I here interrupted him with a smile.

'See this last, master,' continues he, 'and this hammer; this last and hammer are the two best friends I have in this world; nobody else will be my friend, because I want a friend. The great folks you saw pass by just now have five hundred friends, because they have no occasion for them; now, while I stick to my good friends here, I am very contented; but when I ever so little run after sights and fine things, I begin to hate my work; I grow sad, and have no heart to mend shoes any longer.'

'This discourse only served to raise my curiosity to know more of a man whom nature had thus formed into a philosopher. I therefore insensibly led him into a history of his adventures.

'I have lived', said he, 'a wandering sort of a life now five and fifty years; here to-day, and gone to-morrow; for it was my misfortune, when I was young, to be fond of changing.'

'You have been a traveller, then, I presume,' interrupted I.

'I cannot boast much of travelling,' continued he, 'for I have never left the parish in which I was born but three times in my life, that I can remember; but then there is not a street in the whole neighbourhood, that I have not lived in, at some time or another. When I began to settle, and to take to my business in one street, some unforeseen misfortune or a desire of trying my luck elsewhere, has removed me, perhaps, a whole mile away from my former customers, while some more lucky cobbler would come into my place, and make a handsome fortune among friends of my making; there was one who actually died in a stall, that I had left, worth seven pounds seven shillings, all in hard gold, which he had quilted into the waistband of his breeches.'

I could not but smile at these migrations of a man by the fireside, and continued to ask if he had ever been married.

'Aye, that I have, master,' replied he, 'for sixteen long years; and a weary life I had of it, Heaven knows. My wife took it into her head, that the only way to thrive in this world was to save money; so, though our comings in were but about three shillings a week, all that ever she could lay her hands upon she used to hide away from me, though we were obliged to starve the whole week after for it.

'The first three years we used to quarrel about this every day, and I always got the better; but she had a hard spirit, and still continued to hide as usual: so that I was at last tired of quar-relling and getting the better, and, she scraped and scraped at pleasure, till I was almost starved to death. Her conduct drove me at last in despair to the alehouse; here I used to sit with people, who hated home like myself, drank, while I had money left, and ran in score, when anybody would trust me; till at last the landlady, coming one day with a long bill, when I was from home, and putting it into my wife's hands, the length of it effectually broke her heart. I searched so the whole stall, after she was dead, for money; but she had hidden it so effectually, that, with all my pains, I could never find a farthing.'

By this time my shoe was mended, and, satisfying the poor artist for his trouble, and rewarding him besides for his informa-tion, I took my leave, and returned home to lengthen out the amusement his conversation afforded, by communicating it to my friend. Adieu.

P. L., Aug. 12, 1760.

# LETTER XX

## The Fear Of Mad Dogs Ridiculed

To the same.

Indulgent Nature seems to have exempted this island from many of those epidemic evils, which are so fatal in other parts of the world. A want of rain, but for a few days beyond the expected season, in China, spreads famine, desolation, and terror, over the whole country; the winds that blow from the brown bosom of the western desert are impregnated with death in every gale: but, in this fortunate land of Britain, the inhabitant courts health in every breeze, and the husbandman ever sows in joyful expectation.

But, though the nation be exempt from real evils, think not, my friend, that it is more happy on this account than others. They are afflicted, it is true, with neither famine nor pestilence, but then there is a disorder peculiar to the country, which every season makes strange ravages among them; it spreads with pestilential rapidity, and infects almost every rank of people; what is still more strange, the natives have no name for this peculiar malady, though well known to foreign physicians by the appellation of epidemic terror.

A season is never known to pass, in which the people are not visited by this cruel calamity in one shape or another, seemingly different, though ever the same: one year it issues from a baker's shop in the shape of a sixpenny loaf; the next, it takes the appearance of a comet with a fiery tail; a third, it threatens like a flat-bottomed boat and a fourth, it carries consternation at the bite of a mad dog. The people, when once infected, lose their relish for happiness, saunter about with looks of despondence, ask after the calamities of the day, and receive no comfort but in heightening each other's distress. It is insignificant how remote or near, how weak or powerful, the object of terror may be; when once they resolve to fright and be frighted, the merest trifles sow consternation and dismay: each proportions his fears, not to the object, but to the dread he discovers in the countenance of others; for, when once the fermentation is begun, it goes on of itself, though the original cause be discontinued, which first set it in motion.

A dread of mad dogs is the epidemic terror which now prevails; and the whole nation is at present actually groaning under the malignity of its influence. The people sally from their houses with that circumspection, which is prudent in such as expect a mad dog at every turning. The physician publishes his prescription, the beadle prepares his halter, and a few of unusual bravery arm themselves with boots and buff gloves, in order to face the enemy, if he should offer to attack them. In short, the whole people stand bravely upon their defence, and seem, by their present spirit, to show a resolution of not being tamely bit by mad dogs any longer.

Their manner of knowing whether a dog be mad or no somewhat resembles the ancient European custom of trying witches. The old woman suspected was tied hand and foot, and thrown into the water. If she swam, then so she was instantly carried off to be burnt for a witch; if she sunk, then indeed she was acquitted of the charge, but drowned in the experiment. In the same manner, a crowd gather round a dog suspected of madness, and they begin by teasing the devoted animal on every side: if he attempts to stand upon the defensive and bite, then he is unanimously found guilty, for 'a mad dog always snaps at everything'; if, on the contrary, he strives to cape by running away, then he can expect no compassion, for 'mad dogs always run straight forward before them'.

It is pleasant enough for a neutral being like me, who have no share in these ideal calamities, to mark the stages of this national disease. The terror at first feebly enters with a disregarded story of a little dog, that had gone through a neighbouring village, that was thought to be mad by several that had seen him. The next account comes, that a mastiff ran through a certain town, and had bit five geese, which immediately ran mad, foamed at the bill, and died in great agonies soon after. Then comes an affecting history of a little boy bit in the leg, and gone down to be dipt in the salt water. When the people have sufficiently shuddered at that, they are next congealed with a frightful account of a man, who was said lately to have died from a bite he had received some years before. This relation only prepares the way for another still more hideous, as how the master of a family, with seven small children, were all bit by a mad lapdog; and how the poor father first perceived the infection by casing for a draught of water, where he saw the lapdog swimming in the cup.

When epidemic terror is thus once excited, every morning comes loaded with some new disaster; as, in stories of ghosts, each loves to hear the account, though it only serves to make him uneasy, so here each listens with eagerness, and adds to the tidings new circumstances of peculiar horror. A lady, for instance, in the country, of very weak nerves, has been frighted by the barking of a dog; and this, alas, too frequently happens. The story soon is improved and spreads, that a mad dog had frighted a lady of distinction. These circumstances begin to grow terrible, before they have reached the neighbouring village, and there the report is, that a lady of quality was bit by a mad mastiff. This account every moment gathers new strength, and grows more dismal, as it approaches the capital; and, by the time it has arrived in town, the lady is described, with wild eyes, foaming mouth, running mad upon all-four, barking like a dog, biting her servants, and at last smothered between two beds by the advice of her doctors; while the mad mastiff is in the meantime ranging the whole country over, slavering at the mouth, and seeking whom he may devour.

My landlady, a good-natured woman, but a little credulous, waked me some mornings ago before the usual hour, with horror and astonishment in her looks: she desired me, if I had any regard for my safety, to keep within; for a few days ago so dismal an accident had happened, as to put all the world upon their guard. A mad dog down in the country, she assured me, had bit a farmer, who, soon becoming mad, ran into his own yard, and bit a fine brindled cow; the cow quickly became as mad as the man, began to foam at the mouth, and raising herself up, walked about on her hind legs, sometimes barking like a dog, and sometimes attempting to talk like the farmer. Upon examining the grounds of this story, I found my landlady had it from one neighbour, who had it from another neighbour, who heard it from very good authority.

Were most stories of this nature thoroughly examined, it would be found that numbers of such as have been said to suffer were no way injured; and that of those, who have been actually bitten, not one in an hundred was bit by a mad dog. Such accounts in general, therefore, only serve to make the people miserable by false terrors, and sometimes fright the patient into actual frenzy, by creating those very symptoms they pretended to deplore.

But, even allowing three or four to die in a season of this terrible death (and four is probably too large a concession), yet still it is not considered, how many are preserved in their health and in their property, by this devoted animal's services. The midnight robber is kept at a distance; the insidious thief is often detected;

the healthful chase repairs many a worn constitution; and the poor man finds in his dog a willing assistant, eager to lessen his toil, and content with the smallest retribution.

'A dog,' says one of the English poets, 'is an honest creature, and I am a friend to dogs.' Of all the beasts that graze the lawn or hunt the forest, a dog is the only animal that, leaving his fellows, attempts to cultivate the friendship of man: to man he looks in all his necessities with a speaking eye for assistance; exerts for him all the little service in his power with cheerfulness and pleasure; for him bears famine and fatigue with patience and resignation; no injuries can abate his fidelity; no distress induce him to forsake his benefactor; studious to please, and fearing to offend, he is still an humble steadfast dependant, and in him alone fawning is not flattery. How unkind, then, to torture this faithful creature, who has left the forest to claim the protection of man! How ungrateful a return to the trusty animal for all his services! Adieu.

P. L., Aug. 29, 1760.

# LETTER XXI

## The Shabby Beau, The 'Man In Black, The Chinese Philosopher, & C, At Vauxhall

From Lien Chi Altangi to Fum Hoam, First President of the Ceremonial Academy at Pekin in China.

The people of London are as fond of walking, as our friends at Pekin of riding; one of the principal entertainments of the citizens here, in summer, is to repair about nightfall to a garden not far from town, where they walk about, show their best clothes and best faces, and listen to a concert provided for the occasion.

I accepted an invitation, a few evenings ago, from my old friend, the Man in Black, to be one of a party that was to sup there; and at the appointed hour waited upon him at his lodgings. There I found the company assembled, and expecting my arrival. Our party consisted of my friend, in superlative finery, his stockings rolled, a black velvet waistcoat, which was formerly new, and a gray wig combed down in imitation of hair; a pawnbroker's widow, of whom, by the by, my friend was a professed admirer, dressed out in green damask, with three gold rings on every finger; Mr. Tibbs, the second rate beau I have formerly described; together with his lady, in flimsy silk, dirty gauze instead of linen, and an hat as big as an umbrella.

Our first difficulty was in settling how we should set out. Mrs. Tibbs had a natural aversion to the water, and the widow, being a little in flesh, as warmly protested against walking; a coach was therefore agreed upon; which being too small to carry five, Mr. Tibbs consented to sit in his wife's lap.

In this manner, therefore, we set forward, being entertained by the way with the bodings of Mr. Tibbs, who assured us he did not expect to see a single creature for the evening above the degree of a cheesemonger; that this was the last night of the gardens, and that consequently we should be pestered with the nobility and entry from Thames Street and Crooked Lane; with several other prophetic ejaculations, probably inspired by the uneasiness of his situation.

The illuminations began before we arrived, and I must confess that, upon entering the gardens, I found every sense overpaid with more than expected pleasure: the lights everywhere glimmering through the scarcely moving trees; the full-bodied concert bursting on the stillness of the night, the natural concert of the birds, in the more retired part of the grove, vying with that which was formed by art; the company gaily dressed, looking satisfaction, and the tables spread with various delicacies—all conspired to fill my imagination with the visionary happiness of the Arabian lawgiver, and lifted me into an ecstasy of admiration.

'Head of Confucius,' cried I to my friend, 'this is fine! This unites rural beauty with courtly magnificence! If we except the virgins of immortality, that hang on every tree, and may be plucked at every desire, I do not see how this falls short of Mahomet's Paradise!'

We were called to a consultation by Mr. Tibbs and the rest of the company, to know in what manner we were to lay out the evening to the greatest advantage. Mrs. Tibbs was for keeping the genteel walk of the garden, where, she observed, there was always the very best company; the widow, on the contrary, who came but once a season, was for securing a good standing place to see the waterworks, which, she assured us, would begin in less than an hour at farthest; a dispute therefore began, and, as it was managed between two of very opposite characters, it threatened to grow more bitter at every reply. Mrs. Tibbs wondered how people could pretend to know the polite world, who had received all their rudiments of breeding behind a counter: to which the other replied, that, though some people sat behind counters, yet they could sit at the head of their own tables too, and carve three good dishes of hot meat, whenever they thought proper; which was more than some people could say for themselves, that hardly knew a rabbit and onions from a green goose and gooseberries.

It is hard to say where this might have ended, had not the husband, who probably knew the impetuosity of his wife's disposition, proposed to end the dispute by adjourning to a box, and try if there was anything to be had for supper that was supportable. To this we all consented; but here a new distress arose: Mr. and Mrs. Tibbs would sit in none but a genteel box, a box where they might see and be seen, one, as they expressed it, in the very focus of public view; but such a box was not easy to be obtained, for, though we were perfectly convinced of our own gentility, and the gentility of our appearance, yet we found it a difficult matter to persuade the keepers of the boxes to be of our opinion; they chose to reserve genteel boxes for what they judged more genteel company.

At last, however, we were fixed, though somewhat obscurely, and supplied with the usual entertainment of the place. The widow found the supper excellent, but Mrs. Tibbs thought everything detestable.

'Come, come, my dear,' cries the husband, by way of consolation, 'to be sure we can't find such dressing here so as we have at Lord Crump's or Lady Crimp's; but, for Vauxhall dressing, it is pretty good: it is not their victuals, indeed, I find fault with, but their wine; their wine,' cries he, drinking off a glass, 'indeed, is most abominable.'

By this last contradiction, the widow was fairly conquered in point of politeness. She perceived now that she had no pretensions in the world to taste; her very senses were vulgar, since she had praised detestable custard, and smacked at wretched wine; she was therefore content to yield the victory, and for the rest of the night to listen and improve. It is true, she would now and then forget herself, and confess she was pleased; but they soon brought her back again to miserable refinement. She once praised the painting of the box, in which we were sitting, but was soon convinced that such paltry pieces ought rather to excite horror than satisfaction; she ventured again to commend one of the singers, but Mrs. Tibbs soon let her know, in the style of a connoisseur, that the singer in question had neither ear, voice, nor judgment.

Mr. Tibbs, now willing to prove that his wife's pretensions to music were just, entreated her to favour the company with a song; but to this she gave a positive denial.

'For you know very well, my dear,' says she, 'that I am not in voice to-day; and, when one's voice is not equal to one's judgment, what signifies singing? Besides, as there is no accompaniment, it would be but spoiling music.

All these excuses, however, were overruled by the rest of the company, who, though one would think they already had music enough, joined in the entreaty. But particularly the widow, now willing to convince the company of her breeding, pressed so warmly, that she seemed determined to take no refusal. At last, then, the lady complied, and, after humming for some minutes, began with such a voice, and such affectation, as, I could perceive, gave but little satisfaction to any except her husband. He sat with rapture in his eye, and beat time with his hand on the table.

You must observe, my friend, that it is the custom of this country, when a lady or gentleman happens to sing, for the company to sit as mute and motionless as statues. Every feature, every limb, must seem to correspond in fixed attention; and, while the song continues, they are to remain in a state of universal petrifaction. In this mortifying situation we had continued for some time, listening to the song, and looking with tranquillity, when the master of the box came to inform us, that the waterworks were going to begin. At this information I could instantly perceive the widow bounce from her seat; but, correcting herself, she sat down again, repressed by motives of good breeding. Mrs. Tibbs, who had seen the waterworks an hundred times, resolving not to be interrupted, continued her song without any share of mercy, nor had the smallest pity on our impatience. The widow's face, I own, gave me high entertainment; in it I could plainly read the struggle she felt between good breeding and curiosity: she talked of the waterworks the whole evening before, and seemed to have come merely in order to see them; but then she could not bounce out in the very middle of a song, for that would be forfeiting all pretensions to high life, or high-lived company, ever after. Mrs. Tibbs, therefore, kept on singing, and we continued to listen, till at last, when the song was just concluded, the waiter came to inform us that the waterworks were over.

'The waterworks over!' cried the widow; 'The waterworks over already! That's impossible! They can't be over so soon!'

'It is not my business', replied the fellow, 'to contradict your ladyship; I'll run again and see.'

He went, and soon returned with a confirmation of the dismal tidings. No ceremony could now bind my friend's disappointed mistress: she testified her displeasure in the openest manner; in short, she now began to find fault in turn, and at last insisted upon going home, just at the time that Mr. and Mrs. Tibbs assured the company that the polite hours were going to begin, and that the ladies would instantaneously be entertained with the horns. Adieu.

P. L., Sept. 2, 1760.

# LETTER XXII

## The Behaviour Of A Shopkeeper
## And His Journeyman

From Lien Chi Altangi o Fum Hoam, First President of the
Ceremonial Academy at Pekin in China.

The shops of London are as well furnished, as those of Pekin.
Those of London have a picture hung at their door, informing the
passengers what they have to sell, as those at Pekin have a board,
to assure the buyer that they have no intent to cheat him.

I was this morning to buy silk for a nightcap. Immediately upon
entering the mercer's shop, the master and his two men, with wigs
plastered with powder, appeared to ask my commands. They were
certainly the civilest people alive; if I but looked, they flew to the
place where I cast my eye; every motion of mine sent them running round the whole shop for my satisfaction. I informed them
that I wanted what was good, and they showed me not less than
forty pieces; and each was better than the former, the prettiest
pattern in nature, and the fittest in the world for nightcaps.

'My very good friend,' said I to the mercer, 'you must not
pretend to instruct me in silks; I know these in particular to be
no better than your mere flimsy bungees.'

'That may be,' cried the mercer, who, I afterwards found, had never contradicted a man in his life: 'I cannot pretend to say but they may; but, I can assure you, my Lady Trail has had a sacque from this piece this very morning.'

'But, friend,' said I, 'though my lady has chosen a sacque from it, 'I see no necessity that I should wear it for a nightcap.'

'That may be,' returned he again; 'yet what becomes a pretty lady, will at any time look well on a handsome gentleman.'

This short compliment was thrown in so very seasonably upon my ugly face, that even though I disliked the silk, I desired him to cut me off the pattern of a nightcap.

While this business was consigned to his journeyman, the master himself took down some pieces of silk still finer than any I had yet seen and, spreading them before me, 'There,' cries he, 'there's beauty; my Lord Snake-skin has bespoke the fellow to this for the birthnight this very morning; it would look charmingly in waistcoats.'

'But I don't want a waistcoat,' replied I.

'Not want a waistcoat!' returned the mercer; 'then I would advise you to buy one: when waistcoats are wanted, you may depend upon it they will come dear. Always buy before you want, and you are sure to be well used, as they say in Cheapside.'

There was so much justice in his advice, that I could not refuse taking it; besides, the silk, which was really a good one, increased the temptation; so I gave orders for that too.

As I was waiting to have my bargains measured and cut, which, I know not how, they executed but slowly, during the interval, the mercer entertained me with the modern manner of some of the nobility receiving company in their morning gowns.

'Perhaps, sir,' adds he, 'you have a mind to see what kind of silk is universally worn.'

Without waiting for my reply, he spreads a piece before me, which might be reckoned beautiful even in China. 'If the nobility,' continues he, 'were to know I sold this to any under a Right Honourable, I should certainly lose their custom; you see, my lord, it is at once rich, tasty, and quite the thing.'

'I am no lord,' interrupted I. 'I beg pardon,' cried he; 'but be pleased to remember, when you intend buying a morning gown, that you had an offer from me of something worth money. Conscience, sir, conscience is my way of dealing; you may buy a morning gown now, or you may stay till they become dearer and less fashionable; but it is not my business to advise.'

In short, most reverend Fum, he persuaded me to buy a morning gown also, and would probably have persuaded me to have bought half the goods in his shop, if I had stayed long enough, or was furnished with sufficient money.

Upon returning home, I could not help reflecting, with some astonishment, how this very man, with such a confined education and capacity, was yet capable of turning me as he thought proper, and moulding me to his inclinations. I knew he was only answering his own purposes, even while he attempted to appear solicitous about mine; yet, by a voluntary infatuation, a sort of passion, compounded of vanity and good-nature, I walked into the snare with my eyes open, and put myself to future pain in order to give him immediate pleasure. The wisdom of the ignorant somewhat resembles the instinct of animals; it is diffused in but a very narrow sphere, but, within that circle, it acts with vigour, uniformity, and success. Adieu.

P. L., Sept. 22, 1760.

# LETTER XXIII

## The Races Of Newmarket Ridiculed
## Description Of A Cart-Race

To the same.

Of all the places of amusement, where gentlemen and ladies are entertained, I have not been yet to visit Newmarket. This, I am told, is a large field, where, upon certain occasions, three or four horses are brought together, then set a-running and that horse which runs fastest wins the wager.

This is reckoned a very polite and fashionable amusement here, much more followed by the nobility than partridge fighting at Java, or paper kites in Madagascar: several of the great here, I am told, understand as much of farriery as their grooms; and a horse, with any share of merit, can never want a patron among the nobility.

We have a description of this entertainment almost every day in some of the gazettes, as for instance: 'On such a day the Give and Take Plate was run for between his Grace's Crab, his Lordship's Periwinkle, and Squire Smackem's Slamerkin. All rode their own horses. There was the greatest concourse of nobility that has been known here for several seasons. The odds were in favour of Crab in the beginning; but Slamerkin, after the first heat, seemed to have the match hollow: however, it was soon seen that Periwinkle improved in wind, which at last turned out accordingly; Crab was run to a standstill, Slamerkin was knocked up, and Periwinkle was brought in with universal applause.' Thus, you see, Periwinkle received universal applause, and, no doubt, his Lordship came in for some share of that praise which was so liberally bestowed upon Periwinkle. Sun of China! How glorious must the senator appear in his cap and leather breeches, his whip crossed in his mouth, and thus coming to the goal, amongst the shouts of grooms, jockeys, pimps, stable-bred dukes, and degraded generals!

From the description of this princely amusement, now transcribed, and from the great veneration I have for the characters of its principal promoters, I make no doubt but I shall look upon a horse-race with becoming reverence, predisposed as I am by a similar amusement, of which I have lately been a spectator; for just now I happened to have an opportunity of being present at a cart race.

Whether this contention between three carts of different parishes was promoted by a subscription among the nobility, or whether the grand jury, in council assembled, had gloriously combined to encourage plaustral merit, I cannot take upon me to determine; but certain it is, the whole was conducted with the utmost regularity and decorum, and the company, which made a brilliant appearance, were universally of opinion that the sport was high, the running fine, and the riders influenced by no bribe.

It was run on the road from London to a village called Brentford, between a turnip-cart, a dust-cart, and a dung-cart; each of the owners condescending to mount, and be, his own driver. The odds at starting were, Dust against Dung, five to four; but, after half a mile's going, the knowing ones found themselves all on the wrong side, and it was Turnip against the field, brass to silver.

Soon, however, the contest became more doubtful; Turnip indexed kept the way, but it was perceived that Dung had better bottom. The road re-echoed with the shouts of the specta-tors. 'Dung against Turnip! Turnip against Dung!' was now the universal cry; neck and neck; one rode lighter, but the other had more judgement. I could not but particularly observe the ardour, with which the fair sex espoused the cause of the different riders, on this occasion: one was charmed with the unwashed beauties of Dung; another was captivated with the patibulary aspect of Turnip; while, in the meantime, unfortunate gloomy Dust, who came whipping behind, was cheered by the encouragement of some, and pity of all.

The contention now continued for some time, without a possibility of determining to whom victory designed the prize. The winning post appeared in view, and he who drove the turnip-cart assured himself of success; and successful he might have been, had his horse been as ambitious as he; but, upon approaching a turn from the road, which led homewards, the horse fairly stood still, and refused to move a foot farther. The dung-cart had scarce time to enjoy this temporary triumph, when it was pitched headlong into a ditch by the way-side, and the rider left to wallow in congenial mud. Dust, in the meantime, soon came up, and not being far from the post, came in, amidst the shouts and acclamations of all the spectators, and greatly caressed by all the quality of Brentford. Fortune was kind only to one, who ought to have been favourable to all; each had peculiar merit, each laboured hard to earn the prize, and each richly deserved the cart he drove.

I do not know whether this description may not have antici-pated that, which I intended giving of Newmarket. I am told, there is little else to be seen even there. There may be some minute differences in the dress of the spectators, but none at all in their understandings; the quality of Brentford are as remark-able for politeness and delicacy, as the breeders of Newmarket. The quality of Brentford drive their own carts, and the honourable fraternity at Newmarket ride their own horses. In short the matches in one place are as rational as those in the other; and it is more than probable, that turnips, dust, and dung are all that can be found to furnish out description in either.

Forgive me, my friend; but a person like me, bred up in a philosophic seclusion, is apt to regard, perhaps with too much asperity, those occurrences, which sink man below his station in nature, and diminish the intrinsic value of humanity. Adieu.

P. L., Oct. 24, 1760.

# LETTER XXIV

## The Folly Of The Western Parts Of Europe, In Employing The Russians To Fight Their Battles

From Fum Hoam to Lien Chi Altangi.

You tell me the people of Europe are wise; but where lies their wisdom? You say they are valiant too; yet I have some reasons to doubt of their valour. They are engaged in war among each other, yet apply to the Russians, their neighbours and ours, for assistance.

Cultivating such an alliance argues at once imprudence and timidity. All subsidies, paid for such an aid, is strengthening the Russians, already too powerful, and weakening the employers, already exhausted by intestine commotions.

I cannot avoid beholding the Russian empire as the natural enemy of the more western parts of Europe; as an enemy already possessed of great strength, and, from the nature of the government, every day threatening to become more powerful. This extensive empire, which, both in Europe and Asia, occupies almost a third of the world, was, about two centuries ago, divided into separate kingdoms and dukedoms, and, from such a division, consequently feeble. Since the times, however, of

Johan Basilides, it has increased in strength and extent; and those untrodden forests, those innumerable savage animals, which formerly covered the face of the country, are now removed, and colonies of mankind planted in their room. A kingdom, thus enjoying peace internally, possessed of an unbounded extent of dominion, and learning the military art at the expense of others abroad, must every day grow more powerful; and it is probable we shall hear Russia, in future times, as formerly, called the Officina Gentium.

It was long the wish of Peter, their great monarch, to have a fort in some of the western parts of Europe; many of his schemes and treaties were directed to this end, but, happily for Europe, he failed in them all. A fort in the power of this people would be like the possession of a floodgate; and, whenever ambition, interest, or necessity prompted, they might then be able to deluge the whole western world with a barbarous inundation.

Believe me, my friend, I cannot sufficiently condemn the politicians of Europe, who thus make this powerful people arbitrators in their quarrel. The Russians are now at that period between refinement and barbarity, which seems most adapted to military achievement; and, if once they happen to get footing in the western parts of Europe, it is not the feeble efforts of the sons of effeminacy and dissension that can serve to remove them. The fertile valley and soft climate will ever be sufficient inducements to draw whole myriads from their native deserts, the trackless wild, or snowy mountain.

History, experience, reason, nature expand the book so of wisdom before the eyes of mankind, but they will not read. We have seen with terror a winged phalanx of famished locusts, each singly contemptible, but from multitude become hideous, cover, like clouds, the face of day, and threaten the whole world with ruin. We have seen them settling on the fertile plains of India and Egypt, destroying in an instant the labours and the hopes of nations; sparing neither the fruit of the earth nor the verdure of the fields, and changing into a frightful desert landscapes of once luxuriant beauty. We have seen myriads of ants, issuing together from the southern desert, like a torrent whose source was inexhaustible, succeeding each other without end, and renewing their destroyed forces with unwearied perseverance, bringing desolation wherever they came, banishing men and animals, and, when destitute of all subsistence, in heaps infecting the wilderness which they had made. Like these have been the migrations of men. When as yet savage, and almost resembling their brute partners in the forest, subject like them only to the instincts of nature, and directed by hunger alone in the choice of an abode, how have we seen whole armies starting wild at once from their forests and their dens. Goths, Huns, Vandals, Saracens, Turks, Tartars, myriads of men, animals in human form, without country, without name, without laws, overpowering by numbers all opposition, ravaging cities, overturning empires, and, after having destroyed whole nations, and spread extensive desolation, how have we seen them sink oppressed by some new enemy, more barbarous and even more unknown than they! Adieu.

P. L., Oct. 31, 1760.

# LETTER XXV

## Ladies Advised To Get Husbands;
## A Story To This Purpose

From Lien Chi Altangi to Fum Hoam, First President of the
Ceremonial Academy at Pekin in China.

As the instruction of the fair sex in this country is entirely
committed to the care of foreigners; as their language masters,
music masters, hair-frizzers, and governesses, are all from abroad,
I had some intentions of opening a female academy myself,
and made no doubt, as I was quite a foreigner, of meeting a
favourable reception.

In this, I intended to instruct the ladies in all the conjugal
mysteries: wives should be taught the art of managing husbands,
and maids, the skill of properly choosing them; I would teach
a wife how far she might venture to be sick, without giving
disgust; she should be acquainted with the great benefits of the
cholic in the stomach, and all the thorough-bred insolence of
fashion; maids should learn the secret of nicely distinguishing
every competitor; they should be able to know the difference
between a pedant and a scholar, a citizen and a prig, a squire and
his horse, a beau and his monkey; but, chiefly, they should be

taught the art of managing their smiles, from the contemptuous simper to the long laborious laugh.

But I have discontinued the project; for what would signify teaching ladies the manner of governing or choosing husbands, when marriage is at present so much out of fashion, that a lady is very well off, who can get any husband at all? Celibacy now prevails in every rank of life; the streets are crowded with old bachelors, and the houses with ladies who have refused good offers, and are never likely to receive any for the future.

The only advice, therefore, I could give the fair sex, as things stand at present, is to get husbands as fast as they can. There is certainly nothing in the whole creation, not even Babylon in ruins, more truly deplorable than a lady in the virgin bloom of sixty-three, or a battered so unmarried beau, who squibs about from place to place, showing his pigtail wig and his ears. The one appears to my imagination in the form of a double nightcap or a roll of pomatum; the other, in the shape of an electuary, or a box of pills.

I would once more, therefore, advise the ladies to get husbands. I would desire them not to discard an old lover without very sufficient reasons, nor treat the new with ill-nature, till they know him false; let not prudes allege the falseness of the sex, coquettes, the pleasures of long courtship, or parents, the necessary preliminaries of penny for penny. I have reasons that would silence even a casuist in this particular. In the first place, therefore, I divide the subject into fifteen heads, and then sic argumentor——But, not to give you and myself the spleen, be contented at present with an Indian tale.

'In a winding of the river Amidar, just before it falls into the Caspian Sea, there lies an island, unfrequented by the inhabitants of the continent. In this seclusion, blest with all that wild uncultivated nature could bestow, lived a princess and her two daughters. She had been wrecked upon the coast, while her children as yet were' fonts, who, of consequence, though grown up, were entirely unacquainted with man. Yet, inexperienced as the young ladies were in the opposite sex, both early discovered symptoms, the one of prudery, the other of being coquette. The eldest was ever learning maxims of wisdom and discretion from her mamma, while the youngest employed all her hours in gazing at her own face in a neighbouring fountain.

'Their usual amusement in this solitude was fishing: their mother had taught them all the secrets of the art; she showed them which were the most likely places to throw out the line, what baits were most proper for the so various seasons, and the best manner to draw up the finny prey, when they had hooked it. In this manner they spent their time, easy and innocent, till, one day, the princess, being indisposed, desired them to go and catch her a sturgeon or a shark for supper, which she fancied might sit easy on her stomach. The daughters obeyed, and clapping on a gold fish, the usual bait on those occasions, went and sat upon one of the rocks, letting the gilded hook glide down with the stream.

'On the opposite shore, farther down, at the mouth of the river, lived a diver for pearls, a youth who, by long habit in his trade, was almost grown amphibious; so that he could remain whole hours at the bottom of the water, without ever fetching breath. He happened to be at that very instant diving, when the ladies were fishing with the gilded hook. Seeing therefore the bait, which to him had the appearance of real gold, he was resolved to seize the prize; but, both his hands being already filled with pearl oysters, he found himself obliged to snap at it with his mouth: the consequence is easily imagined; the hook, before unperceived, was instantly fastened in his jaw, nor could he, with all his efforts or his floundering, get free.

'Sister,' cries the youngest princess, 'I have certainly caught a monstrous fish; I never perceived anything struggle so at the end of my line before; come and help me to draw it in.'

They both now, therefore, assisted in fishing up the diver on shore; but nothing could equal their surprise on seeing him.

'Bless my eyes!' cries the prude, 'what have we got here? This is a very odd fish, to be sure; I never saw anything in my life look so queer: what eyes, what terrible claws, what a monstrous snout! I have read of this monster somewhere before; it certainly must be a tanlang, that eats women; let us throw it back again into the sea, to where we found it.'

'The diver, in the meantime, stood upon the beach at the end of the line, with the hook in his mouth, using every art that he thought could best excite pity, and particularly looking extremely tender, which is usual in such circumstances. The coquette, therefore, in some measure influenced by the innocence of his looks, ventured to contradict her companion.

'Upon my word, sister,' says she, 'I see nothing in the animal so very terrible, as you are pleased to apprehend; I think it may serve well enough for a change. Always sharks, and sturgeons, and lobsters, and crawfish, make me quite sick. I fancy a slice of this, nicely grilladed, and dressed up with shrimp sauce, would be very pretty eating. I fancy mamma would like a bit with pickles above all things in the world; and, if it should not sit easy on her stomach, it will be time enough to discontinue it, when found disagreeable, you know.'

'Horrid!' cries the prude; 'would the girl be poisoned? I tell you it is a tanlang; I have read of it in twenty places. It is everywhere described as being the most pernicious animal that ever infested the ocean. I am certain it is the most insidious, ravenous creature in the world, and is certain destruction, if taken internally.'

'The youngest sister was now therefore obliged to submit: both assisted in drawing the hook with some violence from the diver's jaw; and he, finding himself at liberty, bent his breast against the broad wave, and disappeared in an instant.

Just at this juncture the mother came down to the beach, to know the cause of her daughters' delay; they told her every circumstance, describing the monster they had caught. The old lady was one of the most discreet women in the world; she was called the black-eyed princess, from two black eyes she had received in her youth, being, a little addicted to boxing in her liquor.

'Alas, my children,' cries she, 'what have you done! the fish you caught was a man-fish: one of the most tame domestic animals in the world. We could have let him run and play about the garden, and he would have been twenty times more entertaining, than our squirrel or monkey.'

'If that be all,' says the young coquette, 'we will fish for him again. If that be all, I'll hold three toothpicks to one pound of snuff, and catch him, whenever I please.'

'Accordingly they threw in their line once more, but with all their gilding, and paddling, and assiduity, they could never after catch the diver. In this state of solitude and disappointment they continued for many years, still fishing, but without success; till at last the Genius of the place, in pity to their distresses, changed the prude into a shrimp, and the coquette into an oyster.' Adieu.

P. L., Nov. 14, 1760.

# LETTER XXVI

## The Fondness Of Some To Admire The Writings Of Lords

To the same.

It is surprising what an influence titles shall have upon the mind, even though these titles be of our own making. Like children, we dress up the puppets in finery, and then stand in astonishment at the plastic wonder. I have been told of a rat-catcher here, who strolled for a long time about the villages near town, without finding any employment; at last, however, he thought proper to take the title of his Majesty's Rat-catcher in ordinary, and thus succeeded beyond his expectations: when it was known that he caught rats at court, all were ready to give him countenance and employment.

But of all the people, they who make books seem most perfectly sensible of the advantage of titular dignity. All seem convinced, that a book written by vulgar hands can neither instruct nor improve; none but kings, chams, and mandarins can write with any probability of success. If the titles inform me right, not only kings and courtiers, but emperors themselves, in this country, periodically supply the press.

A man here who should write, and honestly confess that he wrote, for bread, might as well send his manuscript to fire the baker's oven; not one creature will read him: all must be court-bred poets, or pretend at least to be court-bred, who can expect to please. Should the caitiff fairly avow a design of emptying our pockets and filling his own, every reader would instantly forsake him; even those who write for bread themselves would combine to worry him, perfectly sensible that his attempts only served to take the bread out of their mouths.

And yet this silly prepossession the more amazes me, when I consider, that almost all the excellent productions of wit, that have appeared here, were purely the offspring of necessity. Their Drydens, Butlers, Otways, and Farquhars were all writers for bread. Believe me, my friend, hunger has a most amazing faculty of sharpening the genius; and he who, with a full belly, can think like a hero, after a course of fasting, shall rise to the sublimity of a demi-god.

But what will most amaze is, that this very set of men, who are now so much depreciated by fools, are, however, the very best writers they have among them at present. For my own part, were I to buy a hat, I would not have it from a stocking-maker, but a hatter; were I to buy shoes, I should not go to the tailor's for that purpose. It is just so with regard to wit: did I, for my life, desire to be well served, I would apply only to those, who made it their trade, and lived by it. You smile at the oddity of my opinion: but be assured, my friend, that wit is in some measure mechanical; and that a man long habituated to catch at even its resemblance, will at last be happy enough to possess the substance. By a long habit of writing he acquires a justness of thinking, and a mastery of manner, which holiday writers, even with ten times his genius, may vainly attempt to equal.

How then are they deceived, who expect from title, dignity, and exterior circumstance, an excellence, which is in some measure acquired by habit, and sharpened by necessity! You have seen, like me, many literary reputations, promoted by the influence of fashion, which have scarce survived the possessor; you have seen the poor hardly earn the little reputation they acquired, and their merit only acknowledged, when they were incapable of enjoying the pleasures of popularity: such, however, is the reputation worth possessing; that which is hardly earned is hardly lost. Adieu.

P. L., Jan. 7, 1761.

# LETTER XXVII

## The Philosopher's Son Is Again Separated From His Beautiful Companion

From Hingpo, in Moscow, to Lien Chi Altangi, in London.

Where will my disappointments end? Must I still be doomed to accuse the severity of my fortune, and show my constancy in distress, rather than moderation in prosperity? I had at least hopes of conveying my charming companion safe from the reach of every enemy, and of again restoring her to her native soil. But those hopes are now no more.

Upon leaving Terki, we took the nearest road to the dominions of Russia. We passed the Ural mountains, covered with eternal snow, and traversed the forests of Ufa, where the prowling bear and shrieking hyaena keep an undisputed possession. We next embarked upon the rapid river Bulija, and made the best of our way to the banks of the Wolga, where it waters the fruitful valleys of Casan.

There were two vessels in company, properly equipped and armed, in order to oppose the Wolga pirates, who, we were informed, infested this river. Of all mankind, these pirates are the most terrible. They are composed of the criminals and outlawed peasants of Russia, who fly from the forests, that lie along the banks of the Wolga, for protection. Here they join in parties, lead a savage life, and have no other subsistence but plunder. Being derived of houses, friends, or a fixed habitation, they become more terrible even than the tiger, and as insensible to all the feelings of humanity. They neither give quarter to those they conquer, nor receive it, when overpowered themselves. The severity of the laws against them serves to increase their barbarity, and seems to make them a neutral species of beings, between the wildness of the lion and the subtlety of the man. When taken alive, their punishment is hideous. A floating gibbet is erected, which is let run down with the stream; here, upon an iron hook stuck under their ribs, and upon which the whole weight of their body depends, they are left to expire in the most terrible agonies, some being thus found to linger several days successively.

We were but three days' voyage from the confluence of this river into the Wolga, when we perceived at a distance behind us an armed bark coming up, with the assistance of sails and oars, in order to attack us. The dreadful signal of death was hung upon the mast, and our captain with his glass could easily discern them to be pirates. It is impossible to express our consternation on this occasion; the whole crew instantly came together to consult the properest means of safety. It was, therefore, soon determined to send off our women and valuable commodities in one of our vessels, and that the men should stay in the other, and boldly oppose the enemy. This resolution was soon put into execution, and I now reluctantly parted from the beautiful Zelis, for the first time since our retreat from Persia. The vessel, in which she was, disappeared to my longing eyes, in proportion as that of the pirates approached us. They soon came up, but, upon examining our strength, and perhaps sensible of the manner in which we had sent off our most valuable effects, they seemed more eager to pursue the vessel we had sent away, than attack us. In this manner they continued to harass us for three days, still endeavouring to pass us without fighting. But, on the fourth day, finding it entirely impossible, and despairing to seize the expected booty, they desisted from their endeavours, and left us to pursue our voyage without interruption.

Our joy on this occasion was great; but soon a disappointment, more terrible, because unexpected, succeeded. The bark, in which our women and treasure were sent off, was wrecked upon the banks of the Wolga, for want of a proper number of hands to manage her, and the whole crew carried by the peasants up the country. Of this, however, we were not sensible till our arrival at Moscow; where, expecting to meet our separated bark, we were informed of its misfortune, and our loss.

Need I paint the situation of my mind on this occasion? Need I describe all I feel, when I despair of beholding the beautiful Zelis more? Fancy had dressed the future prospect of my life in the gayest colouring; but one so unexpected stroke of fortune has robbed it of every charm. Her dear idea mixes with every scene of pleasure, and, without her presence to enliven it, the whole becomes tedious, insipid, insupportable. I will confess —now that she is lost, I will confess, I loved her; nor is it in the power of time, or of reason, to erase her image from my heart. Adieu.

P. L., Oct. 27, 1760.

# LETTER XXVIII

## A Description Of The Courts Of Justice In Westminster Hall

From Lien Chi Altangi to Fum Hoam.

I had some intentions lately of going to visit Bedlam, the place where those who go mad are confined. I went to wait upon the Man in Black to be my conductor; but I found him preparing to go to Westminster Hall, where the English hold their courts of justice. It gave me some surprise to find my friend engaged in a lawsuit, but more so when he informed me that it had been depending for several years.

'How is it possible', cried I, 'for a man who knows the world to go to law? I am well acquainted with the courts of justice in China: they resemble rat-traps every one of them; nothing more easy than to get in, but to get out again is attended with some difficulty, and more cunning, than rats are generally found to possess!'

'Faith,' replied my friend, 'I should not have gone to law, but that I was assured of success before I began; things were presented to me in so alluring a light, that I thought, by barely declaring myself a candidate for the prize, I had nothing more to do than to enjoy the fruits of the victory. Thus I have been upon the eve of an imaginary triumph, every term, these ten years; have travelled forward with victory ever in my view, but ever out of reach; however, at present I fancy we have hampered our antagonist in such a manner, that, without some unforeseen demur, we shall this very day lay him fairly on his back.' 'If things be so situated,' said I, 'I don't care if I attend you to the courts, and partake in the pleasure of your success. But, prithee,' continued I, as we set forward, , 'what reasons have you to think an affair at last concluded, which has given you so many former disappointments?'

'My lawyer tells me', returned he, 'that I have Salkeld and Ventris strong in my favour, and that there are no less than fifteen cases in point.'

'I understand', said I; 'those are two of your judges who have already declared their opinions.'

'Pardon me,' replied my friend, 'Salkeld and Ventris are lawyers who some hundred years ago gave their opinions on cases similar to mine: these opinions which make for me, my lawyer is to cite; and those opinions which look another way are cited by the lawyer employed by my antagonist: as I observed, I have Salkeld and Ventris for me; he has Coke and Hale for him; and he that has most opinions is most likely to carry his cause.'

'But where is the necessity', cried I, 'of prolonging a suit by citing the opinions and reports of others, since the same good sense, which determined lawyers in former ages, may serve to guide your judges at this day? They at that time gave their opinions only from the light of reason; your judges have the same light at present to direct them; let me even add, a greater, as, in former ages, there were many prejudices, from which the present is happily free. If arguing from authorities be exploded so from every other branch of learning, why should it be particularly adhered to in this? I plainly foresee how such a method of investigation must embarrass every suit, and even perplex the student; ceremonies will be multiplied, formalities must increase, and more time will thus be spent in learning the arts of litigation, than in the discovery of right.' 'I see', cries my friend, 'that you are for a speedy administration of justice; but all the world will grant, that the more time that is taken up in considering any subject, the better it will be understood. Besides, it is 'the boast of an Englishman, that his property is secure, and all the world will grant, that a deliberate adminis-tration of justice is the best way to secure his property. Why have we so many lawyers, but to secure our property? Why so many formalities, but to secure our property? Not less than one hundred thousand families live in opulence, elegance, and ease, merely by securing our property.'

'To embarrass justice', returned I, 'by a multiplicity of laws, or to hazard it by a confidence in our judges, are, I grant, the oppo-site rocks on which legislative wisdom has ever split : in one case, the client resembles that emperor, who is said to have been suffocated with the bed-clothes, which were only designed to keep him warm; in the other, to that town, which let the enemy take possession of its walls, in order to show the world how little they depended upon aught but courage for safety. But, bless me, what numbers do I see here—all in black—how is it possible that half this multitude can find employment?'

'Nothing so easily conceived,' returned my companion; 'they live by watching each other. For instance, the catchpole watches the man in debt, the attorney watches the catchpole, the coun-sellor watches the attorney, the solicitor the counsellor, and all find sufficient employment.'

'I conceive you,' interrupted I; 'they watch each other, but it is the client that pays them all for watching: it puts me in mind of a Chinese fable, which is entitled: 'Five Animals At A Meal'.

'A grasshopper, filled with dew, was merrily singing under a shade; a whangam, that eats grasshoppers, had marked it for its prey, and was just stretching forth to devour it; a serpent, that had for a long time fed only on whangams, was coiled up to fasten on the whangam; a yellow bird was just upon the wing to dart upon the serpent; a hawk had just stooped from above to seize the yellow bird; all were intent on their prey, and unmindful of their danger: so the whangam ate the grasshopper, the serpent ate the whangam, the yellow bird the serpent, and the hawk the yellow bird; when, sousing from on high, a vulture gobbled up the hawk, grasshopper, whangam, and all in a moment.' I had scarce finished my fable, when the lawyer came to inform my friend, that his cause was put off till another term, that money was wanted to retain, and that all the world was of opinion, that the very next hearing would bring him off victorious. 'If so, then,' cries my friend, 'I believe it will be my wisest way to continue the cause for another term; and, in the meantime, my friend here and I will go and see Bedlam.' Adieu.

P. L., Nov. 28, 1760.

# LETTER XXIX

## The Chinese Philosopher Begins To Think Of Quitting England

From Lien Chi Altangi to a Merchant in Amsterdam.

I have just received a letter from my son, in which he informs me of the fruitlessness of his endeavours to recover the lady, with whom he fled from Persia. He strives to cover, under the appearance of fortitude, a heart torn with anxiety and disappointment. I have offered little consolation, since that but too frequently feeds the sorrow, which it pretends to deplore, and strengthens the impression, which nothing but the external rubs of time and accident can thoroughly efface.

He informs me of his intentions of quitting Moscow the first opportunity, and travelling by land to Amsterdam. I must, therefore, upon his arrival, entreat the continuance of your friendship, and beg of you to provide him with, proper directions for finding me in London. You can scarcely be sensible of the joy I expect upon seeing him once more; the ties between the father and the son among us of China are much more closely drawn, than with you of Europe.

The remittances sent me from Argun to Moscow came in safety. I cannot sufficiently admire that spirit of honesty which prevails through the whole country of Siberia: perhaps the savages of that desolate region are the only untutored people of the globe, that cultivate the moral virtues, even without knowing that their actions merit praise. I have been told surprising things of their goodness, benevolence, and generosity; and the uninterrupted commerce between China and Russia serves as a collateral confirmation.

'Let us', says the Chinese lawgiver, 'admire the rude virtues of the ignorant, but rather imitate the delicate morals of the polite.' In the country where I reside, though honesty and benevolence be not so congenial, yet art supplies the place of nature. Though here every vice is carried to excess, yet every virtue is practised also with unexampled superiority. A city like this is the soil for great virtues and great vices: the villain can soon improve herein the deepest mysteries of deceiving; and the practical philosopher can every day meet new incitements to mend his honest intentions. There are no pleasures, sensual or sentimental, which this city does not produce; yet, I know not how, I could not be content to reside here for life. There is something so seducing in that spot, in which we first had existence, that nothing but it can please. Whatever vicissitudes we experience in life, however we toil, or wheresoever we wander, our fatigued wishes still recur to home for tranquillity; we long to die in that spot which gave us birth, and, in that pleasing expectation, opiate every calamity.

You now, therefore, perceive that I have some intentions of leaving this country; and yet my designed departure fills me with reluctance and regret. Though the friendships of travellers are generally more transient than vernal snows, still I feel an uneasiness at breaking the connections I have formed since my arrival; particularly, I shall have no small pain in leaving my usual companion, guide, and instructor.

I shall wait for the arrival of my son, before I set out. He shall be my companion in every intended journey for the future; in his company I can support the fatigues of the way with redoubled ardour, pleased at once with conveying instruction, and exacting obedience. Adieu.

P. L., Jan. 19, 1761.

# LETTER XXX

## The Intended Coronation Described

From Lien Chi Altangi to Fum Hoam.

The time for the young king's coronation approaches. The great and the little world look forward with impatience. A knight from the country, who has brought up his family to see and be seen on this occasion, has taken all the lower part of the house where I lodge. His wife is laying in a large quantity of silks, which the mercer tells her are to be fashionable next season; and miss, her daughter, has actually had her ears bored previous to the ceremony. In all this bustle of preparation, I am considered as mere lumber, and have been shoved up two storeys higher, to make room for others, my landlady seems perfectly convinced are my betters; but whom, before me, she is contented with only calling very good company.

The Little Beau, who has now forced himself into my intimacy, was yesterday giving me a most minute detail of the intended procession. All men are eloquent upon their favourite topic; and this seemed peculiarly adapted to the size and turn of his understanding. His whole mind was blazoned over with a variety of glittering images: coronets, escutcheons, lace, fringe, tassels, stones, bugles, and spun glass.

'Here', cried he, 'Garter is to walk; and there Rouge Dragon marches with the escutcheons on his back. Here Clarencieux moves forward; and there Blue Mantle disdains to be left behind. Here the Aldermen march two and two; and there the undaunted Champion of England, no way terrified at the very numerous appearance of gentlemen and ladies, rides forward in complete armour, and, with an intrepid air, throws down his glove. Ah!' continued he, 'should any be so hardy as to take up that fatal glove, and so accept the challenge, we should see fine sport; the Champion would show him no mercy; he would soon teach him all his passes, with a witness. However, I am afraid we shall have none willing to try it – try him upon the approaching occasion, for two reasons: first, because, his antagonist would stand a chance of being killed in the single combat; and, secondly, because, if he escapes the champion's arm, he would certainly be hanged for treason. No, no; I fancy none will be so hardy as to dispute it with a champion like him, inured to arms; and we shall probably see him prancing unmolested away, holding his bridle thus in one hand, and brandishing his dram-cup in the other.'

Some men have a manner of describing, which only wraps the subject in more than former obscurity; thus I was unable, with all my companion's volubility, to form a distinct idea of the intended procession. I was certain that the inauguration of a king should be conducted with solemnity and religious awe; and I could not be persuaded that there was much solemnity in this description.

'If this be true,' cried I to myself, 'the people of Europe surely have a strange manner of mixing solemn and fantastic images together; pictures at once replete with burlesque and the sublime. At a time when the king enters into the most solemn compact with his peoples nothing surely should be admitted to diminish from the real majesty of the ceremony. A ludicrous image, brought in at such a time, throws an air of ridicule upon the whole. It someway resembles a picture I have seen, designed by Albert Durer, where, amidst all the solemnity of that awful scene, a deity judging, and a trembling world awaiting the decree, he has introduced a merry mortal, trundling a scolding wife to hell in a wheelbarrow. My companion, who mistook my silence, during this interval of reflection, for the rapture of astonishment, proceeded to describe those frivolous parts of the show, that most struck his imagination; and to assure me, that, if I stayed in this country some months longer, I should see fine things.

'For my own part,' continued he, 'I know already of fifteen suits of clothes, that would stand on one end with gold lace, all designed to be first shown there; and, as for diamonds, rubies, emeralds, and pearls, we shall see them as thick as brass nails in a sedan chair. And then we are all to walk so majestically, thus: this foot always behind the foot before. The ladies are to fling nosegays; the court poets to scatter verses; the spectators are to be all in full dress; Mrs. Tibbs in a new sacque, ruffles, and trenched hair: look where you will, one thing finer than another; Mrs. Tibbs curt-sies to the Duchess; her Grace returns the compliment with a bow. 'Largess!'; cries the herald. 'Make room!' cries the gentleman usher. 'Knock him down!' cries the guard. Ah!' continued he, amazed at his own description, 'what an astonishing scene of grandeur can art produce from the smallest circumstance, when it thus actually turns to wonder one man putting on another man's hat!'

I now found his mind was entirely set upon the fopperies of the pageant, and quite regardless of the real meaning of such costly preparations. 'Pageants', says Bacon, 'are pretty things; but we should rather study to make them elegant than expen-sive.' Processions, cavalcades, and all that fund of gay frippery, furnished out by tailors, barbers, and tirewomen, mechanically influence the mind into veneration. An emperor in his nightcap would not meet with half the respect of an emperor with a glittering crown. Politics resemble religion; attempting to divest either of ceremony is the most certain method of bringing either into contempt. The weak must have their inducements to admiration as well as the wise; and it is the business of a sensible government to impress all ranks with a sense of subordination, whether this be effected by a diamond buckle or a virtuous edict, a sumptuary law or a glass necklace.

This interval of reflection only gave my companion spirits to begin his description afresh; and, as a greater inducement to raise my curiosity, he informed me of the vast sums that were given by the spectators for places. 'That the ceremony must be fine', cries he, 'is very evident from the fine price that is paid for seeing it. Several ladies have assured me, they could willingly part with one eye, rather than be prevented from looking on with the other. Come, come,' continues he, 'I have a friend, who, for my sake, will supply us with places at the most reasonable rates; I'll take care you shall not be imposed upon; and he will inform you of the use, finery, rapture, splendour, and enchantment of the whole ceremony, better than I.'

Follies often repeated lose their absurdity, and assume the appearance of reason. His arguments were so often and so strongly enforced, that I had actually some thoughts of becoming a spectator. We accordingly went together to bespeak a place; but guess my surprise, when the man demanded a purse of gold for a single seat! I could hardly believe him serious upon making the demand.

'Prithee, friend,' cried I, 'after I have paid twenty pounds for sitting here an hour or two, can I bring a part of the coronation back?'

'No, sir.'

'How long can I live upon it, after I have come away?'

'Not long, sir.'

'Can a coronation clothe, feed, or fatten me?'

'Sir,' replied the man, 'you seem to be under a mistake; all that you can bring away is the pleasure of having it to say, that you saw the coronation.'

'Blast me!' cries Tibbs, 'if that be all, there is no need of paying for that; since I am resolved to have that pleasure, whether I am there or no!'

I am conscious, my friend, that this is but a very confused description of the intended ceremony. You may object, that I neither settle rank, precedency, nor place; that I seem ignorant whether Gules walks before or behind Garter; that have neither mentioned the dimensions of a lord's cap, nor measured the length of a lady's tail. I know your delight is in minute description: and this I am unhappily disqualified from furnishing; yet, upon the whole, I fancy it will be no way comparable to the magnificence of our late Emperor Whangti's procession, when he was married to the moon, at which Fum Hoam himself presided in person. Adieu.

P. L., Feb. 10, 1761.

# LETTER XXXI

## On The Different Sects In England, Particularly Methodists

To the same.

Religious sects in England are far more numerous than in China. Every man who has interest enough to hire a conventicle here may set up for himself, and sell off a new religion. The sellers of the newest pattern at present give extreme good bargains, and let their disciples have a great deal of confidence for very little money.

Their shops are more frequented, and their customers every day increasing; for people are naturally fond of going to paradise at as small expense as possible.

Yet you must not conceive this modern sect as differing in opinion from those of the established religion; difference of opinion indeed, formerly divided their sectaries, and sometimes drew their armies to the field. White gowns and black mantles, flapped hats and crossed pocket-holes were once the obvious causes of quarrel; men then had some reason for fighting; they knew what they fought about: but at present they are arrived at such refinement in religion making, that they have actually formed a new sect without a new opinion; they quarrel for opinions they both equally defend; they hate each other, and that is all the difference between them.

But though their principles are the same, their practice is somewhat different. Those of the established religion laugh, when they are pleased, and their groans are seldom extorted, but by pain or danger. The new sect, on the contrary, weep for their amusement, and use little music, except a chorus of sighs and groans, or tunes that are made to imitate groaning. Laughter is their aversion; lovers court each other from the Lamentations; the bridegroom approaches the nuptial couch in sorrowful solemnity, and the bride looks more dismal than an understaker's shop. Dancing round the room is with them running in a direct line to the devil; and, as for gaming, though but in jest, they would sooner play with a rattlesnake's tail, than finger a dice-box.

By this time you will perceive that I am describing a sect of enthusiasts, and you have already compared them with the Faquirs, Brahmins, and Talapoins of the East. Among these, you know, are generations that have never been known to smile, and voluntary affliction makes up all the merit they can boast of. Enthusiasm in every country provides the same effects; stick the Faquir with pins, or confine the Brahmin to a vermin hospital; spread the Talapoin on the ground, or load the sectary's brow with contrition: those worshippers, who discard the light of reason, are ever gloomy; their fears increase in proportion to their ignorance, as men are continually under apprehensions, who walk in darkness.

Yet there is still a stronger reason for the enthusiasts being an enemy to laughter; namely, his being himself so proper an object of ridicule. It is remarkable, that the propagators of false doctrines have ever been averse to mirth, and always begin by recommending gravity, when they intended to disseminate imposture. Fohi, the idol of China, is represented as having never laughed; Zoroaster, the leader of the Brahmins, is said to have laughed but twice, upon his coming into the world, and upon his leaving it; and Mahomet himself, though a lover of pleasure, was a professed opposer of gaiety. Upon a certain occasion, telling his followers that they would appear all naked at the resurrection, his favourite wife presented such an assembly as immodest and unbecoming. 'Foolish woman!' cried the grave prophet, 'though the whole assembly be naked, on that day they shall have forgotten to laugh.' Men like him opposed ridicule, because they knew it to be a most formidable antagonist; and preached up gravity, to conceal their own want of importance.

Ridicule has ever been the most powerful enemy of enthusiasm, and, properly, the only antagonist that can be opposed to it with success. Persecution only serves to propagate new religions: they acquire fresh vigour beneath the executioner and the axe, and, like some vivacious insects, multiply by dissection. It is also impossible to combat enthusiasm with reason; for, though it makes a show of resistance, it soon eludes the pressure, refers you to distinctions not to be understood, and feelings which it cannot explain. A man, who would endeavour to fix an enthusiast by argument, might as well attempt to spread quicksilver with his fingers. The only way to conquer a visionary is to despise him; the stake, the faggot, and the disputing doctor, in some measure, ennoble the opinions they are brought to oppose: they scare harmless against innovating pride; contempt alone is truly dreadful. Hunters generally know the most vulnerable part of the beasts they pursue, by the care which every animal takes to defend the side which is weakest; on what side the enthusiast is most vulnerable may be known by the care, which he takes in the beginning to work his disciples into gravity, and guard them against the power of ridicule.

When Philip the Second was king of Spain, there was a contest in Salamanca between two orders of friars for superiority. The legend of one side contained more extraordinary miracles, but the legend of the other was reckoned most authentic. They reviled each other, as is usual in disputes of divinity; the people were divided into factions, and a civil war appeared unavoidable. In order to prevent such an imminent calamity, the combatants were prevailed upon to submit their legends to the fiery trial, and that which came forth untouched by the fire was to have the victory, and to be honoured with a double share of reverence. Whenever the people flock to see a miracle, it is a hundred to one but that they see a miracle; incredible, therefore, were the numbers that were gathered round upon this occasion. The friars on each side approached, and confidently threw their respective legends into the flames, when, lo, to the utter disappointment of all the assembly, instead of a miracle, both legends were consumed! Nothing, but this turning both parties into contempt, could have prevented the effusion of blood. The people now laughed at their former folly, and wondered why they fell out. Adieu.

P. L., March 11, 1761.

# LETTER XXXII

## An Election Described,

To the same.

The English are at present employed in celebrating a feast, which becomes general every seventh year; the parliament of the nation being then dissolved, and another appointed to be chosen. This solemnity falls infinitely short of our Feast of the Lanterns in magnificence and splendour; it is also surpassed by others of the East in unanimity and pure devotion; but no festival in the world can compare with it for eating. Their eating, indeed, amazes me; had I five hundred heads, and were each head furnished with brains, yet would they all be insufficient to compute the number of cows, pigs, geese, and turkeys, which, upon this occasion, die for the good of their country.

To say the truth, eating seems to make a grand ingredient in all English parties of zeal, business, or amusement. When a church is to be built, or an hospital endowed, the directors assemble, and, instead of consulting upon it, they eat upon it, by which means the business goes forward with success. When the poor are to be relieved, the officers appointed to dole out public charity assemble, and eat upon it. Nor has it ever been known that they filled the bellies of the poor, till they had previously satisfied their own. But, in the election of magistrates, the people seem to exceed all bounds: the merits of a candidate are often measured by the number this treats; his constituents assemble, eat upon him, and lend their applause, not to his integrity or sense, but to the quantities of his beef and brandy.

And yet I could forgive this people their plentiful meals on this occasion, as it is extremely natural for every man to eat a great deal, when he gets it for nothing but what amazes me is, that all this good living no way contributes to improve their good humour. On the contrary, they seem to lose their temper as they lose their appetites; every morsel they swallow, and every glass they pour down, serves to increase their animosity. Many an honest man, before as harmless as a tame rabbit, when loaded with a single election dinner, has become more dangerous than a charged culverin. Upon one of these occasions I have actually seen a bloody-minded man-milliner sally forth at the head of a mob, determined to face a desperate pastrycook, who was general of the opposite party.

But you must not suppose they are without a pretext for thus beating each other. On the contrary, no man here is so uncivilized as to beat his neighbour, without producing very sufficient reasons. One candidate,, for instance, treats with gin, a spirit of their own manufacture; another always drinks brandy, imported from abroad. Brandy is a wholesome liquor; gin, a liquor wholly their own. This, then, furnishes an obvious cause of quarrel; whether it be most reasonable to get drunk with gin, or get drunk with brandy. The mob meet upon the debate; fight themselves sober; and then draw off to get drunk again, and charge for another encounter. So that the English may now properly be said to be engaged in war; since, while they are subduing their enemies abroad, they are breaking each other's heads at home.

I lately made an excursion to a neighbouring village, in order to be a spectator of the ceremonies practised upon this occasion. I left town in company with three fiddlers, nine dozen of hams, and a corporation poet, which were designed as reinforcements to the gin-drinking party. We entered the town with a very good face; the fiddlers, no way intimidated by the enemy, kept handling their arms up the principal street. By this prudent manoeuvre, they took peaceable possession of their headquarters, amidst the shouts of multitudes, who seemed perfectly rejoiced at hearing their music, but above all at seeing their bacon.

I must own, I could not avoid being pleased to see all ranks of people, on this occasion, levelled into an equality, and the poor, in some measure, enjoying the primitive privileges of nature. If there was any distinction shown, the lowest of the people seemed to receive it from the rich. I could perceive a cobbler with a levee at his door, and a haberdasher giving audience from behind his counter. But my reflections were soon interrupted by a mob, who demanded whether I was for the distillery or the brewery. As these were terms with which I was totally unacquainted, I chose at first to be silent; however, I know not what might have been the consequence of my reserve, had not the attention of the mob been called off to a skirmish between a brandy-drinker's cow and a gindrinker's mastiff, which turned out, greatly to the satisfaction of the mob, in favour of the mastiff.

This spectacle, which afforded high entertainment, was at last ended by the appearance of one of the candidates, who came to harangue the mob; he made a very pathetic speech upon the late excessive importation of foreign drams, and the downfall of the distillery; I could see some of the audience shed tears. He was accompanied in his procession by Mrs. Deputy and Mrs. Mayoress. Mrs. Deputy was not in the least in liquor; and as for Mrs. Mayoress, one of the spectators assured me in my ear that— she was a very fine woman, before she had the small-pox.

Mixing with the crowd, I was now conducted to the hall where the magistrates are chosen: but what tongue can describe this scene of confusion; the whole crowd seemed equally inspired with anger, jealousy, politics, patriotism, and punch. I remarked one figure that was carried up by two men upon this occasion. I at first began to pity his infirmities as natural, but soon found the fellow so drunk, that he could not stand; another made his appearance to give his vote, but, though he could stand, he actually lost the use of his tongue, and remained silent; a third, who, though excessively drunk, could both stand and speak, being asked the candidate's name for whom he voted, could be prevailed upon to make no other answer, but 'Tobacco and brandy'. In short, an election hall seems to be a theatre, where every passion is seen without disguise; a school, where fools may readily become worse, and where philosophers may gather wisdom. Adieu.

P. L., April 3, 1761.

# LETTER XXXIII

## A City Night-Piece

To the same.

The clock just struck two; the expiring taper rises and sinks in the socket; the watchman forgets the hour in slumber; the laborious and the happy are at rest; and nothing wakes but meditation, guilt, revelry, and despair. The drunkard once more fills the destroying bowl; the robber walks his midnight round; and the suicide lifts his guilty arm against his own sacred person.

Let me no longer waste the night over the page of antiquity, or the sallies of contemporary genius, but: pursue the solitary walk, where vanity, ever changing, but a few hours past, walked before me; where she kept up the pageants, and now, like a froward child, seems hushed with her own importunities.

What a gloom hangs all round! The dying lamp feebly emits a yellow gleam; no sound is heard but of the chiming clock, or the distant watch-dog. All the bustle of human pride is forgotten; an hour like this may well display the emptiness of human vanity.

There will come a time, when this temporary solitude may be made continual; and the city itself, like its inhabitants, fade away, and leave a desert in its room.

What cities as great as this have once triumphed in existence; had their victories as great, joy as just, and as unbounded; and, with short-sighted presumption, promised themselves immortality! Posterity can hardly trace the situation of some: the sorrowful traveller wanders over the awful ruins of others; and, as he beholds, he learns wisdom, and feels the transience of every sublunary possession.

'Here', he cries, 'stood their citadel, now grown over with weeds; there their senate house, but now the haunt of every noxious reptile; temples and theatres stood here, now only an undistinguished heap of ruin. They are fallen; for luxury and avarice first made them feeble. The rewards of the state were conferred on amusing, and not on useful, members of society. Their riches and opulence invited the invaders, who, though at first repulsed, returned again, conquered by perseverance, and at last swept the defendants into undistinguished destruction.'

How few appear in those streets which, but some few hours ago, were crowded! And those, who appear, now no longer wear their daily mask, nor attempt to hide their lewdness or their misery.

But who are those who make the streets their couch, and find a short repose from wretchedness at the doors of the opulent? These are strangers, wanderers, and orphans, whose circumstances are too humble to expect redress, and whose distresses are too great even for pity. Their wretchedness excites rather horror than pity. Some are without the covering even of rags, and others emaciated with disease; the world has disclaimed them; society turns its back upon their distress, and has given them up to nakedness and hunger. These poor shivering females have once seen happier days, and been flattered into beauty. They have been prostituted to the gay luxurious villain, and are now turned out to meet the severity of winter. Perhaps now, lying at the doors of their betrayers, they sue to wretches whose hearts are insensible, or debauchees, who may curse, but will not relieve them.

Why, why was I born a man, and yet see the sufferings of wretches I cannot relieve? Poor houseless creatures! The world will give you reproaches, but will not give you relief. The slightest misfortunes of the great, the most imaginary uneasinesses of the rich, are aggravated with all the power of eloquence, and held up to engage our attention and sympathetic sorrow. The poor weep unheeded, persecuted by every subordinate species of tyranny; and every law, which gives others security, becomes an enemy to them. Why was this heart of mine formed with so much sensibility; or why was not my fortune adapted to its impulse? Tenderness, without a capacity of relieving, only makes the man, who feels it, more wretched than the object, which sues for assistance. Adieu.

The Bee, October 27, 1759.

# LETTER XXXIV

## On The Distresses Of The Poor; Exemplified In The Life Of A Common Soldier

From Lien Chi Altangi to Fum Hoam, First President of the Ceremonial Academy at Pekin in China.

The misfortunes of the great, my friend, are held up to engage our attention, are enlarged upon in tones of declamation, and the world is called upon to gaze at the noble sufferers; they have at once the comfort of admiration and pity.

Yet, where is the magnanimity of bearing misfortunes, when the whole world is looking on? Men in such circumstances can act bravely, even from motives of vanity. He only, who in the vale of obscurity can brave adversity, who, without friends to encourage, acquaintances to pity, or even without hope to alleviate his distresses, can behave with tranquillity and indifference, is truly great; whether peasant or courtier, he deserves admiration, and should be held up for our imitation and respect.

The miseries of the poor are, however, entirely disregarded; though some undergo more real hardships in one day than the great, in their whole lives. It is indeed inconceivable what difficulties the meanest English sailor or soldier endures, without murmuring or regret. Every day to him is a day of misery, and yet he bears his hard fate without repining.

With what indignation do I hear the heroes of tragedy complain of misfortunes and hardships, whose greatest calamity is founded in arrogance and pride! Their severest distresses are pleasures, compared to what many of the adventuring poor every day sustain, without murmuring. These may eat, drink, and sleep; have slaves to attend them, and are sure of subsistence for life; while many of their fellow-creatures are obliged to wander, without a friend to comfort or to assist them, find enmity in every law, and are too poor to obtain even justice.

I have been led into these reflections from accidentally meeting, some days ago, a poor fellow begging at one of the outlets of this town, with a wooden leg. I was curious to learn what had reduced him to his present situation; and, after giving him what I thought proper, desired to know the history of his life and misfortunes, and the manner in which he was reduced to his present distress. The disabled soldier, for such he was, with an intrepidity truly British, leaning on his crutch, put himself into an attitude to comply with my request, and gave me his history as follows:

'As for misfortunes, sir, I cannot pretend to have gone through more than others. Except the loss of my limb, and my being obliged to beg, I don't know any reason, thank Heaven, that I have to complain: there are some who have lost both legs and an eye; but, thank Heaven, it is not quite so bad with me.

'My father was a labourer in the country, and died when I was five years old; so I was put upon the parish. As he had been a wandering sort of a man, the parishioners were not able to tell to what parish I belonged, or where I was born; so they sent me to another parish, and that parish sent me to a third; till at last it was thought I belonged to no parish at all. At length, however, they fixed me. I had some disposition to be a scholar, and had actually learned my letters; but the master of the workhouse put me to business as soon as I was able to handle a mallet.

'Here I lived an easy kind of a life for five years. I only wrought ten hours in the day, and had my meat and drink provided for my labour. It is true, I was not suffered to stir far from the house, for fear I should run away; but what of that? I had the liberty of the whole house, and the yard before the door, and that was enough for me.

'I was next bound out to a farmer, where I was up both early and late; but I ate and drank well, and liked my business well enough, till he died. Being then obliged to provide for myself, I was resolved to go and so seek my fortune. Thus I lived, and went from town to town, working when I could get employment, and starving when I could get none, and might have lived so still; but happening one day to go through a field belonging to a magistrate, I spied a hare crossing the path just before me. I believe the devil put it in my head to fling my stick at it; well, what will you have on't? I killed the hare, and was bringing it away in triumph, when the Justice himself met me; he called me a villain, and collaring me, desired I would give an account of myself. I began immediately to give a full account of all that I knew of my breed, seed, and generation; but, though I gave a very long account, the Justice said I could give no account of myself; so I was indicted, and found guilty of being poor, and sent to Newgate, in order to be transported to the plantations.

'People may say this and that of being in goal; but, for my part, found Newgate as agreeable a place as ever I was in in all my life. I had my bellyful to eat and drink, and did no work; but, alas, this kind of life was too good to last for ever. I was taken out of prison, after five months, put on board of a ship, and sent off with two hundred more. Our passage was but indifferent, for we were all confined in the hold, and died very fast, for want of sweet air and provisions; but, for my part, I did not want meat, because I had a fever all the way: Providence was kind; when provisions grew short, it took away my desire of eating. When we came ashore, we were sold to the planters.

I was bound for seven years, and as I was no scholar—for I had forgot my letters—I was obliged to work among the negroes; and served out my time, as in duty bound to do.

'When my time was expired, I worked my passage home, and glad I was to see old England again, because I so loved my country. O liberty! Liberty! Liberty! That is the property of every Englishman, and I will die in its defence. I was afraid, however, that I should be indicted for a vagabond once more; so I did not much care to go into the country, but kept about town; and did little jobs when I could get them. I was very happy in this manner for some time; till one evening, coming home from work, two men knocked me down, and then desired me to stand still. They belonged to a pressgang; I was carried before the Justice, and as I could give no account of myself (that was the thing that always hobbled me), I had my choice left, whether to go on board a man-of-war, or list for a soldier. I chose to be a soldier; and in this post of a gentleman I served two campaigns in Flanders, was at the battles of Val and Fontenoy, and received but one wound through the breast, which is troublesome to this day.

'When the peace came on, I was discharged; and as I could not work, because my wound was sometimes painful, I listed for a landsman in the East India Company's service. I here fought the French in six pitched battles; and verily believe, that if I could read and write, our captain would have given me promotion, and made me a corporal. But that was not my good fortune; I soon fell sick, and when I became good for nothing, got leave to return home again with forty pounds in my pocket, which I saved in the service. This was at the beginning of the present war, so I hoped to be set on shore, and to have the pleasure of spending my money; but the government wanted men, and I was pressed again, before ever I could set foot on shore.

'The boatswain found me, as he said, an obstinate fellow; he swore that I understood my business perfectly well, but that I shammed Abraham merely to be idle. God knows, I knew nothing of sea business; he beat me without considering what he was about. But still my so forty pounds was some comfort to me under every beating, the money was my comfort, and the money I might have had to this day, but that our ship was taken by the French, and so I lost it all.

'Our crew was carried into a French prison, and many of them died, because they were not used to live in a gaol; but, for my part, it was nothing to me, for I was seasoned. One night, however, as I was sleeping on a bed of boards, with a warm blanket about me (for I always loved to lie well), I was awakened by the boatswain, who had a dark lantern in his hand. 'Jack,' says he to me, 'will you knock out the French sentry's brains?' 'I don't care', says I, striving to keep myself awake, 'if I lend a hand.' 'Then follow me,' says he, 'and I hope we shall do business.' So up I got, and tied my blanket, which was all the clothes I had, about my middle, and went with him to fight the Frenchman. We had no arms; but one Englishman is able to beat five Frenchmen at any time; so we went down to the door, where both the sentries were posted, and, rushing upon them, seized their arms in a moment, and knocked them down. From thence nine of us ran together to the quay, and seizing the first boat we met, got out of the harbour, and put to sea. We had not been here three days, before we were taken up by an English privateer, who was glad of so many good hands; and we consented to run our chance. However, we had not so much luck as we expected. In three days we fell in with a French man-of-war, of forty guns, while we had but twenty-three; so to it we went. The fight lasted for three hours, and I verily believe we should have taken the Frenchman, but unfortunately we lost almost all our men, just as we were going to get the victory. I was once more in the power of the French, and I believe it would have gone hard with me, had I been brought back to my old gaol in Brest; but, by good fortune, we were retaken, and carried to England once more.

'I had almost forgot to tell you, that in this last engagement I was wounded in two places—I lost four fingers of the left hand, and my leg was shot off. Had I had the good fortune to have lost my leg, and use of my hand on board a king's ship, and not a privateer, I should have been entitled to clothing and maintenance during the rest of my life; but that was not my chance: one man is born with a silver spoon in his mouth, and another with a wooden ladle. However, blessed be God, I enjoy good health, and have no enemy in this world that I know of but the French and the Justice of Peace.'

Thus saying, he limped off, leaving my friend and me in admiration of his intrepidity and content; nor could we avoid acknowledging, that an habitual acquaintance with misery is the truest school of fortitude and philosophy. Adieu.

The British Magazine, June, 1760.

# LETTER XXXV

## The Manner Of Travellers In Their Usual Relations Ridiculed

To the same.

My long residence here begins to fatigue me. As every object ceases to be new, it no longer continues to be pleasing; some minds are so fond of variety, that pleasure itself, if permanent, would be insupportable, and we are thus obliged to solicit new happiness, even by courting distress. I only, therefore, wait the arrival of my son to vary this trifling scene, and borrow new pleasure from danger and fatigue. A life, I own, thus spent in wandering from place to place, is at best but empty dissipation. But to pursue trifles is the lot of humanity: and whether we bustle in a pantomime, or strut at a coronation; whether we shout at a bonfire, or harangue in a senate-house; whatever object we follow, it will at last surely conduct us to futility and disappointment. The wise bustle and laugh as they walk in the pageant, but fools bustle and are important; and this, probably, is all the difference between them.

This may be an apology for the levity of my former correspondence; I talked of trifles, and I knew that they were trifles:

to make the things of this life ridiculous, it is only sufficient to call them by their names.

In other respects, I have omitted several striking circumstances in the description of this country, as supposing them either already known to you, or as not being thoroughly known to myself; but there is one omission for which I expect no forgiveness, namely, my being totally silent upon their buildings, roads, rivers, and mountains. This is a branch of science, on which all other travellers are so very prolix, that my deficiency will appear the more glaring. With what pleasure, for instance, do some read of a traveller in Egypt measuring a fallen column with his cane, and finding it exactly five feet and nine inches long; of his creeping through the mouth of a catacomb, and coming out by a different hole from that he entered; of his stealing the finger of an antique statue, in spite of the janizary that watched him; or his adding a new conjecture to the hundred and fourteen conjectures, already published, upon the names of Osiris and Isis.

Methinks I hear some of my friends in China demanding a similar account of London and the adjacent villages; and, if I remain here much longer, it is probable I may gratify their curiosity. I intend, when run dry on other o topics, to take a serious survey of the city wall; to describe that beautiful building the mansion-house; I will enumerate the magnificent squares, in which the nobility chiefly reside, and the royal palaces appointed for the reception of the English monarch; nor will I forget the beauties of Shoe Lane, in which I myself have resided since my arrival. You shall find me no way inferior to many of my brother travellers in the arts of description. At present, however, as a specimen of this way of writing, I send you a few hasty remarks, collected in a late journey I made to Kentish Town, and this in the manner of modern voyagers.

Having heard much of Kentish Town, I conceived a strong desire to see that celebrated place. I could have wished, indeed, to satisfy my curiosity without going thither; but that was impracticable, and therefore I resolved to go. Travellers have two methods of going to Kentish Town: they take coach, which costs ninepence, or they may go afoot, which costs nothing; in my opinion, a coach is by far the most eligible convenience, but I was resolved to go on foot, having considered with myself, that going in that manner would be the cheapest way.

As you set out from Dog-house bar, you enter upon a fine level road railed in on both sides, commanding on the right a small prospect of groves and fields, enamelled with flowers, which would wonderfully charm the sense of smelling, were it not for a dunghill on the left, which mixes its effluvia with their odours. This dunghill is of much greater antiquity than the road; and I must not omit a piece of injustice I was going to commit upon this occasion. My indignation was levelled against the makers of the dunghill, for having brought it so near the road; whereas, it should have fallen upon the makers of the road, for having brought that so near the dunghill.

After proceeding in this manner for some time, a building, resembling somewhat a triumphal arch, salutes so the traveller's view. This structure, however, is peculiar to this country, and vulgarly called a turnpike-gate; I could perceive a long inscription, in large characters, on the front, probably upon the occasion of some triumph, but, being in haste, I left it to be made out by some subsequent adventurer who may happen to travel this way; so, continuing my course to the west, I soon arrived at an unwalled town, called Islington.'

Islington is a pretty neat town, mostly built of brick, with a church and bells; it has a small lake, or rather pond, in the midst, though at present very much neglected. I am told it is dry in summer: if this be the case, it can be no very proper receptacle for fish; of which the inhabitants themselves seem sensible, by bringing all that is eaten there from London.

After having surveyed the curiosities of this fair and beautiful town, I proceeded forward, leaving a fair stone building, called the White Conduit House, on my right. Here the inhabitants of London often assemble to celebrate a feast of hot rolls and butter. Seeing such numbers, each with their little tables before them, employed on this occasion, must, no doubt, be a very amusing sight to the looker-on, but still more so to those who perform in the solemnity.

From hence I parted with reluctance to Pancras, as it is written, or Pancridge, as it is pronounced; but which should be both pronounced and written Pangrace: this emendation I will venture meo arbitrio, in the Greek, language, signifies all, which, added to the English word grace, maketh all grace, or Pangrace; and, indeed, this is a very proper appellation to a place of so much sanctity as Pangrace is universally esteemed. However this be, If you except the parish church and its fine bells, there is little in Pangrace worth the attention of the curious observer.

From Pangrace to Kentish Town is an easy journey of one mile and a quarter; the road lies through a fine champaign country, well watered with beautiful drains, and enamelled with flowers of all kinds, which might contribute to charm every sense, were it not that the odoriferous gales are often more impregnated with dust than perfume.

As you enter Kentish Town, the eye is at once presented with the shops of artificers, such as vendors of candles, small coal, and hair brooms; there are also several august buildings of red brick, with numberless sign posts, or rather pillars, in a peculiar order of architecture. I send you a drawing of several, vide A B C. This pretty town probably borrows its name from its vicinity to the county of Kent; and, indeed, it is not unnatural that it should, as there are only London and the adjacent villages that lie between them. Be this as it will, perceiving night approach, I made a hasty repast on roasted mutton and a certain dried fruit called potatoes, resolving to protract my remarks upon my return; and this I would very willingly have done, but was prevented by a circumstance which, in truth, I had for some time foreseen, for night coming on, it was impossible to take a proper survey of the country, as I was obliged to return home in the dark. Adieu.

# LETTER XXXVI

## The Conclusion

To the same.

After a variety of disappointments, my wishes are at length fully satisfied. My son, so long expected, is arrived; at once, by his presence, banishing my anxiety, and opening a new scene of unexpected pleasure. His improvements in mind and person have far surpassed even the sanguine expectations of a father. I left him a boy, but he is returned a man; pleasing in his person, hardened by travel, and polished by adversity. His disappointment in love, however, had infused an air of melancholy into his conversation, which seemed at intervals to interrupt our mutual satisfaction. I expected that this could find a cure only from time; but fortune, as if willing to load us with her favours, has, in a moment, repaid every uneasiness with rapture.

Two days after his arrival, the Man in Black, with his beautiful niece, came to congratulate us upon this pleasing occasion; but guess our surprise, when my friend's lovely kinswoman was found to be the very captive my son had rescued from Persia, and who had been wrecked on the Wolga, and was carried by the Russian peasants to the port of Archangel. Were I to hold the pen of a novelist, I might be prolix in describing their feelings at so unexpected an interview; but you may conceive their joy without my assistance: words were unable to express their transports; then how can words describe it?

When two young persons are sincerely enamoured of each other, nothing can give me such pleasure as seeing them married: whether I know the parties or not, I am happy at thus binding one link more in the universal chain. Nature has, in some measure, formed me for a match-maker, and given me a soul to sympathize with every mode of human felicity. I instantly, therefore, consulted the Man in Black, whether we might not crown their mutual wishes by marriage: his soul seems formed of similar materials with mine; he instantly gave his consent, and the next day was appointed for the solemnization of their nuptials.

All the acquaintances which I had made since my arrival were present at this gay solemnity. The little Beau was constituted master of the ceremonies, and his wife, Mrs. Tibbs, conducted the entertainment with proper decorum. The Man in Black and the pawnbroker's widow were very sprightly and tender upon this occasion. The widow was dressed up under the direction of Mrs. Tibbs; and, as for her lover, his face was set off by the assistance of a pig-tail wig, which was lent by the little Beau, to fit him for making love with proper formality. The whole company easily perceived that it would be a double wedding before all was over, and, indeed, my friend and the widow seemed to make no secret of their passion; he even called me aside in order to know my candid opinion, whether I did not think him a little too old to be married.

'As for my own part,' continued he, 'I know I am going to play the fool; but all my friends will praise my wisdom, and produce me as the very pattern of discretion to others.'

At dinner everything seemed to run on with good humour, harmony, and satisfaction. Every creature in company thought themselves pretty, and every jest was laughed at. The Man in Black sat next his mistress, helped her plate, chimed her glass, and, jogging her knees and her elbow, he whispered something arch in her ear, on which she patted his cheek; never was antiquated passion so playful, so harmless, and amusing, as between this reverend couple.

The second course was now called for, and, among a variety of dishes, a fine turkey was placed before the widow. The Europeans, you know, carve as they eat; my friend, therefore, begged his mistress to help him to a part of the turkey. The widow, pleased with an opportunity of showing her skill in carving (an art upon which so it seems she piqued herself), began to cut it up by first taking off the leg.

'Madam,' cried my friend, 'if I might be permitted to advise, I would begin by cutting off the wing, and then the leg will come off more easily.'

'Sir,' replies the widow, 'give me leave to understand cutting up a fowl; I always begin with the leg.'

'Yes, madam,' replies the lover; 'but if the wing be the most convenient manner, I would begin with the wing.'

'Sir,' interrupts the lady, 'when you have fowls of your own, begin with the wing if you please, but give me leave to take off the leg; I hope I am not to be taught at this time of day.'

'Madam,' interrupts he, 'we are never too old to be instructed.'

'Old, sir!' interrupts the other. 'Who is old, sir? When I die of age, I know of some that will quake for fear. If the leg does not come off, take the turkey to yourself.'

'Madam,' replied the Man in Black, 'I don't care a farthing whether the leg or wing comes off; if you are for the leg first, why, you shall have the argument, even though it be as I say.'

'As for the matter of that,' cries the widow, 'I don't care a fig whether you are for the leg off or on; and, friend, for the future keep your distance.'

'Oh,' replied the other, 'that is easily done; it is only removing to the other end of the table; and so, madam, your most obedient humble servant.'

Thus was the courtship of an age destroyed in one moment; for this dialogue effectually broke off the match between this respectable couple, that had been but just concluded. The smallest accidents disappoint treaties. However, though it in some measure interrupted the general satisfaction, it no ways lessened the happiness of the youthful couple; and, by the young lady's looks, I could perceive she was not entirely displeased with this interruption.

In a few hours, the whole transaction seemed entirely forgotten, and we have all since enjoyed those satisfactions, which result from a consciousness of making each other happy. My son and his fair partner are fixed here for life; the Man in Black has given them up a small estate in the country, which, added to what I was able to bestow, will be capable of supplying all the real, but not the fictitious, demands of happiness. As for myself, the world being but one city to me, I do not much care in which of the streets I happen to reside; I shall, therefore, spend the remainder of my days in examining the manners of different countries, and have prevailed upon the Man in Black to be my companion. 'They must often change,' says Confucius, 'who would be constant in happiness or wisdom.' Adieu.

P. L., Aug. 14, 1761.